REINHOLD PLASTICS
APPLICATIONS SERIES

ALKYD RESINS

C. R. MARTENS

Assistant Director
Cleveland Technical Service Department
The Sherwin-Williams Co.
Cleveland, Ohio

REINHOLD PUBLISHING CORPORATION

NEW YORK

CHAPMAN & HALL, LTD., LONDON

Printed in the United States of America

Reinhold Plastics
Applications Series

The visitor interest in plastics at the Reinhold booth at the 1956 New York Plastics Exhibition was largely responsible for this series. Now, with even increased interest displayed by visitors to the 1961 New York Plastics Exhibit, the project progresses with increased enthusiasm.

This book on "Alkyd Resins" is the twenty-first in the series and books in preparation cover new materials and many new developments in processing. Among the new materials books will be those on Polycarbonates and Acetal Resins.

The process books will include Premix Molding, Blow Molding, and Extrusion of Plastics.

Despite the introduction of volumes on processing, the general character of the books will remain the same—that is, they will be semi-technical, addressed primarily to engineers, designers, students and, in fact, all practical people in plastics.

With production curves in the plastics field continuing to rise at an astonishing rate, it is with considerable confidence that the series continues with its wider horizon.

HERBERT R. SIMONDS
Editor

TITLES PUBLISHED

PREFACE

The term "alkyd" is a coined name referred to certain groups of polymeric esters as contrasted to other resin groups such as polyamides, silicones, etc., in which the name denotes the chemical composition.

This book presents a review of alkyd resins from the standpoint of chemistry, raw materials, polymer structure, and application. The major portion of the book stresses protective coatings applications since this is the principal use of alkyd resins. They are used extensively in this field because of their excellent "all-around" properties and adaptability by modification to fit almost any application.

The author wishes to express his appreciation to the Sherwin-Williams Company for their help, encouragement, information and photographs supplied for this book. The author is also indebted to many other companies, particularly raw material suppliers, for data, information and photographs.

C. R. MARTENS

Cleveland, Ohio
September, 1961

vii

CONTENTS

1. INTRODUCTION

Alkyd is a term applied to a group of synthetic resins best described as oil-modified polyester resins. This group of materials comprises the reaction products derived from a polyhydric alcohol, a polybasic acid, and fatty monobasic acids.

The term "alkyd" was coined from the "al" of alcohol, the "kyd" being representative of the last syllable of acid. While some of the early usage of the term "alkyd" was applied to unmodified polyesters, the term today usually refers to polymeric esters modified with fatty acids and used in protective coatings.

Alkyds are, therefore, members of a large class of materials known as polymeric esters. They are related to "polyester resins" which are unsaturated polymeric esters dissolved in a polymerizable solvent, such as styrene. These, upon the addition of a peroxide catalyst and heat, cure to an insoluble resin which is used principally in molding applications. Another type of polyester resin is used to produce polyurethane foams. Fibers such as "Dacron" * and films such as "Mylar" * are produced from still another class of polyester resins.

To add to the confusion in terminology, the name alkyd has been used to refer to certain proprietary polyester molding compounds which contain no highly volatile monomer. This, however, is unusual as these materials belong to the class defined as unsaturated polyester resins.

* Registered trade mark E. I. duPont de Nemours & Co., Inc.

Most of the alkyds used today employ phthalic anhydride as the main polybasic acid constituent, polyalcohols such as glycerin and pentaerythritol, and oxidizing or non-oxidizing fatty acids derived from vegetable and animal sources.

History

The history of alkyds is an interesting one, involving many individuals and the introduction of numerous new raw materials [8, 9] (see Table 1.1). The first polymeric ester was discovered accidentally by Berzelius [3] in 1847 by heating glyceryl with tartaric acid. Shortly thereafter in 1853, Berthelot [2] prepared the glyceryl ester of camphoric acid, and Von Bemmelen [13] prepared glyceryl succinate and glyceryl citrate. Smith [12] prepared glyceryl phthalate in 1901 but as these resins were not soluble in any solvent, they were of no practical use. About this time phenol-formaldehyde resins were beginning to be used for electrical insulation and by 1912 "Bakelite" * became a standard insulating material. Laboratories like those of the General Electric Company were investigating other synthetic resins such as polymeric esters at this time [1, 4, 5, 6, 7].

It was found in the glyceryl phthalate reaction that when part of the phthalic anhydride was substituted with a monobasic acid, such as butyric or oleic acid, more flexible resins were obtained. A similar effect was obtained when an aliphatic dibasic acid such as succinic was used. This work also showed that glyceryl phthalate could be modified and flexibilized with castor oil and that high-temperature baking varnishes could be prepared. Because long baking periods at temperatures of 300°F were required to cure their films, they were of little value to the protective coatings industry except for limited electrical use. These coat-

* Trade mark Union Carbide and Carbon Corp.

ings lacked film build, were difficult to pigment and costly because of the high price of phthalic anhydride.

TABLE 1.1. DEVELOPMENT OF ALKYD RESINS.

Date	Accomplishment
1847	Glyceryl tartrate discovered by Berzelius.
1853	Glyceryl ester of camphoric acid made by Berthelot.
1853	Glyceryl succinate and citrate prepared by Von Bemmelen.
1901	Glyceryl phthalate prepared by Smith.
1910	General Electric patents on polymeric esters for use in varnishes, impregnants, and adhesives, by Callahan, Kienle, *et al.*
1914	Arsem prepared glyceryl phthalate modified with oleic acid.
1914	Howell made glyceryl phthalate modified with castor oil.
1916	Vapor-phase process for phthalic anhydride from naphthalene by Gibbs, *et al.*
1920	Modifier for cellulosic finishes.
1927	Drying oil modification of polymeric esters by Kienle, *et al.*
1927	Monoglyceride process for making alkyds by Ott, *et al.*
1929	Modification of glyceryl phthalate by Ellis.
1931	Solvent processing for alkyd manufacture.
1932	Co-condensation of alkyds with phenol-formaldehyde by Honel.
1937	Commercial production of pentaerythritol.
1938	Co-condensation of alkyds with urea-formaldehyde.
1939	Production of dehydrated castor oil.
1941	Production of fumaric acid by fermentation.
1942	Styrenated alkyds.
1945	Commercial production of trimethylol propane and trimethylol ethane.
1947	Synthetic glycerin production.
1956	Commercial production of isophthalic acid.

During World War I the Gibbs-Conover process [10] for the manufacture of phthalic anhydride by the catalytic oxidation of naphthalene was introduced, which made phthalic anhydride available in quantity. In 1917, 138,000 pounds were produced and sold at a price of $4.23 per pound. During the war, because of the high price of shellac, some glyceryl phthalate was used to bond mica flake into sheets for electrical use. The first alkyd resins sold commercially were made by the General Electric Company under the name "Glyptal."

About this time, investigations were in progress on the bodying and drying of linseed and other drying oils. The theory was developed that drying was an intermolecular linking of the conjugated double bonds of the fatty acid of the glyceride molecules by the oxygen of the air. When soluble glyceryl phthalate resins were blended with drying oils they were found to be incompatible. This was overcome by introducing drying fatty acids along with glycerin and phthalic anhydride in the reaction. By this method a homogeneous resin was produced which would convert to an insoluble state on air-drying or heating. These resins were soluble in low-cost aliphatic and aromatic solvents and produced films with good over-all properties such as adhesion, flexibility, and durability.

During this period nitrocellulose lacquers were replacing oleoresinous finishes on automobiles. The fast drying of the lacquer speeded up the finishing of automobiles on the production line. It was found that the proper adhesion of nitrocellulose to metal surfaces required the use of a compatible resin. Natural resins, such as dewaxed dammar, were first used for this purpose. Then rosin-modified alkyds and nondrying oil alkyds were found to be more durable. By 1928 the price of phthalic anhydride had dropped to 16 cents per pound and about one-half million pounds of alkyd resins were produced.

Now began the investigation of alkyds on a large scale for use in the protective coatings field. Durable, tough, flexible, white decorative finishes were required for the home appliance field. Other coating applications were investigated. At first alkyds showed weaknesses such as poor color retention, after-tack, and high acid values. In the past thirty years the problems have been overcome by progress in raw materials, manufacture, and formulation. Initially, alkyds were prepared by the direct interaction of fatty acids, polybasic acid, and polyols. Today alkyds can be produced directly from drying oils using a monoglyceride procedure. Early alkyds were manufactured using a fusion process; today both fusion and solvent processes are used. In 1957

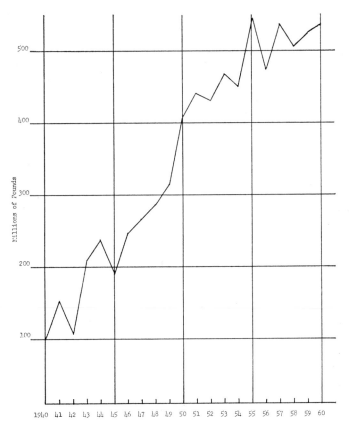

Figure 1.1. Alkyd production in the United States, 1940-1960.

some 543 million pounds of alkyds [14] were produced as shown in Figure 1.1.

During the past thirty years, alkyds have been combined with many other resins and materials such as phenolics, amino resins, styrene, silicones, etc., to increase their range of usefulness in the protective coatings field.

New Raw Materials

The search for improved alkyd resins has encouraged the development of many new raw materials.

In 1937 the commercial production of pentaerythritol from formaldehyde and acetaldehyde started. During World War II the shortage of tung or wood oil stimulated the production of dehydrated castor oil. About 1945 the commercial production of two other polyols, trimethylol-propane and trimethylolethane, was begun. In 1947 synthetic glycerin from petroleum sources went on the market. This stabilized the price of glycerin which, heretofore, was obtained from natural sources such as fats and oils. In 1956 the commercial production of isophthalic acid began which added a unique material to the list of those available for use in alkyds.

Use in Protective Coatings

Most alkyds, as manufactured, are produced in solution form, usually at 50 per cent solids, for ease of handling in the surface coatings field. About 97 per cent of all alkyds produced are consumed in the protective coatings field, and the remainder is used in adhesives, plasticizers, printing inks, textile sizing, molding, etc.

Alkyds [10] are the backbone of the protective coatings industry and recent figures show that about half of all the resins used are alkyds (see Figure 1.2). Alkyds are in great demand because of their low cost and versatility. By modification they can be utilized in a wide variety of applica-

tions. They are used in architectural finishes as odorless flat
wall paints, enamels and exterior trim paints, etc., and in
metal coatings as appliance and automotive finishes, etc.

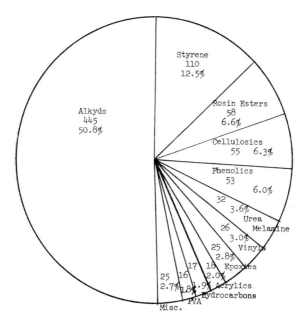

Figure 1.2. Estimated distribution of resins in coatings.

Only about half the alkyds produced are sold on the
open market. Many paint companies make their own alkyd
resins and use them immediately in the production of paint.
At the present time, there are some 95 producers of alkyd
resins in the United States of which about 30 offer their
products for sale, as shown in Table 1.2.

The growth of alkyds has slowed down due to the inroads
of latex polymers into the protective coatings field. However, it would appear at this time that alkyds will continue

to be a primary vehicle used in protective coatings for many years to come.

TABLE 1.2. COMMERCIAL ALKYD PRODUCERS.

Alkydol Laboratories	McCloskey Varnish Co.
Allied Chemical & Dye Corp.	McWhorter Chemicals, Inc.
American Cyanamid Co.	Mol-Rez Div.,
Archer-Daniels-Midland Co.	American Petrochemical Corp.
Calvert-Mt. Winans Co.	C. J. Osborn Co.
Cargill, Inc.	Phenalk Chemicals, Inc.
Cook Paint & Varnish Co.	Reichhold Chemicals, Inc.
Crownoil Chemical Co.	Rohm & Haas Co.
Farac Oil & Chemical Co.	Schenectady Varnish Co.
Farnow, Inc.	Sherwin-Williams Co.
France, Campbell & Darling, Inc.	Specialty Resins Co.
Freeman Chemical Corp.,	Fred'k A. Stresen-Reuter, Inc.
General Electric Co.	U. S. Coatings Co.
Hercules Powder Co.	T. F. Washburn Co.
Jones-Dabney Co.	G. A. Wharry & Co.

References

1. Arsem, W. C., U. S. Patents 1,098,776 and 1,098,777 (June 2, 1914).
2. Berthelot, M. M., *Compt. rend.,* **37**, 398 (1853).
3. Berzelius, J., *Rap. ann.,* **26** (1847).
4. Callahan, M. J., U. S. Patents 1,108,329-30 and 1,108,332 (Aug. 25, 1914); 1,091,627-8 and 1,091,732 (Mar. 31, 1914).
5. Dawson, E. S., U. S. Patent 1,141,944 (June 8, 1915).
6. Friberg, L. H., U. S. Patent 1,119,592 (Dec. 1, 1914).
7. Howell, K. B., U. S. Patent 1,098,728 (June 2, 1914).
8. Kienle, R. H., *Ind. Eng. Chem.,* **21**, 349 (1929).
9. Kienle, R. H., *Ind. Eng. Chem.,* **41**, 726 (1949).
10. Mattiello, J. J., "Protective and Decorative Coatings," Vol. 1, p. 338, New York, John Wiley & Sons, Inc., 1941.
11. Sayre, J. E., *Am. Paint J.,* **42**, No. 32, 80 (1958).
12. Smith, W., *J. Soc. Chem. Ind.,* **20**, 1073 (1901).
13. Von Bemmelen, J., *J. Prakt. Chem.,* **69**, 84 (1856).
14. United States Tariff Commission Reports, "Synthetic Organic Chemicals."

2. GENERAL PROPERTIES

Alkyd resins are based on three fundamental building blocks—polyhydric alcohols, dibasic acids, and oils or fatty acids. Variation in these components and the amounts used give innumerable varieties of resins and vehicles.

Composition versus Performance

Glycerin is still the predominant polyhydric component used in alkyd resins. Any alkyd produced from a whole drying oil will, of course, contain glycerin, as drying oils are triglycerides. However, additional polyalcohol must be incorporated to esterify the dibasic acid, and in many cases more glycerin is required. Pentaerythritol, various glycols, sorbitol, trimethylolethane, and trimethylolpropane are finding increasing use.

Other basic components of alkyds are polybasic acids or anhydrides. The most important of these is phthalic anhydride or acid. Other dibasic acids, such as adipic, azelaic, and sebacic, are being used when more flexibility or greater plasticization is required.

Properties—Effect of Oil

There are a wide number of oils and fatty acids of varying degrees of unsaturation. Variation of this component alone allows us a wide gradation in film properties from a soft, colorless plasticizing film to a hard, tough, tack-free film (see Figures 2.1 and 2.2). In the formation of oil-modified alkyd resins, the degree of polymerization is sufficiently high that only a small amount of oxidative cross-linking is necessary to dry the film. Because of this, less-expensive oils of lower unsaturation can be used to form air-drying alkyds. Oils such as soybean oil and fatty acids from tall oil are of this type.

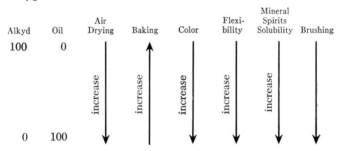

Alkyd	Oil	Air Drying	Baking	Color	Flexi-bility	Mineral Spirits Solubility	Brushing
100	0						
		increase	increase	increase	increase	increase	
0	100						

Figure 2.1. Effect of amount of oil on properties.

Oil	Iodine Value	Drying Time	Color	Gloss Retention
Tung	165			
Linseed	180			
Dehydrated castor	140			
Safflower	145	decrease	increase	increase
Soya	140			
Cottonseed	110			
Coconut	10			

Figure 2.2. Effect of type of oil on properties.

Variation in oil content of the alkyd changes the proportions of aliphatic, aromatic, and polar constituents. This is shown in Figure 2.3 for a glyceryl phthalate alkyd.

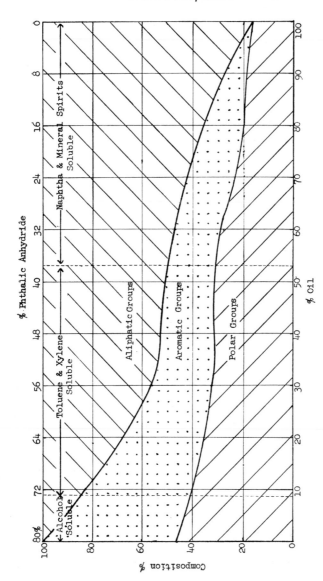

Figure 2.3. Effect of amount of oil in over-all composition of an alkyd. (Glyceryl phthalate alkyd)

The percentage of oil contained in an alkyd classifies the alkyd as to end use since this affects such properties as speed of dry, gloss, color, color retention, etc.

The usual classifications as to oil length for unmodified alkyds are as follows:

	% Oil	% P.A.
Short oil	35-45	> 35
Medium oil	46-55	30-35
Long oil	56-70	20-30
Very long oil	71 up	< 20

Properties—Desirable for Protective Coatings

Alkyds possess many desirable properties required of a vehicle for protective coatings. Low-cost solvents can be used which give ease of application as well as a minimum of odor. Various methods of application such as brush, spray, dip, flowcoat, etc., can be used. Alkyds are ideal vehicles for pigmented coatings because they have:

1. Good wetting and dispersing properties
2. Good stability against colloidal degradation
3. Good tackiness and viscosity suitable for the particular dispersion operation

Alkyd vehicles can be used with most types of pigments. With certain reactive pigments, such as zinc oxide and aluminum paste, alkyds of very low acid value must be used. Alkyd coatings are comparatively low in cost; they have excellent durability, flexibility, gloss retention, and good solvent resistance, toughness, heat resistance, and color retention. The alkali resistance and resistance to ester and ketone solvents of alkyds is not good. A comparison of the film properties of alkyds versus other types of polymers is shown in Table 2.1.

TABLE 2.1. PROPERTIES OF COATING RESINS.

	Alkyd	Alkyd Amine	Styrenated Alkyd	Acrylic	Nitro Cellulose	Catalyzed Epoxy	Epoxy Ester	Phenolic	Silicone	Urethane	Vinyl	Chlorinated Rubber
Exterior durability	E	E	G	E	E	G	G	E	E	E	E	E
Salt spray	E	G	G	E	E	E	E	E	E	E	E	E
Alkali resistance	P	F	F	F	P	E	G	G	P	F	E	G
Solvent aliphatic hydrocarbon	G	E	F	F	F	E	G	E	G	F	E	G
Solvent ester ketones	P	P	P	P	P	G	F	G	P	F	P	P
Flexibility	E	G	G	E	E	F	G	G	F	E	E	G
Impact	G	E	G	E	E	G	E	G	G	E	E	G
Heat resistance	G	G	G	G	E	G	G	E	E	E	E	E
Color retention	G	G	G	E	E	F	G	P	G	G	G	G
Gloss retention	E	G	G	E	G	P	F	F	E	P	F	F

Code: E, excellent; G, good; F, fair; P, poor.
Note: Above ratings are only approximate. Properties vary in each group depending on specific formulation and application and whether air dried or baked.

TABLE 2.2. CHARACTERISTICS OF COMMERCIAL ALKYD RESINS.

Dyal* Alkyd Resins	Per Cent Solids 1%	Solvent	Color Gardner 1933	Viscosity Gardner-Holdt 25°C	Pounds per Gallon	Min Per Cent Phthalic Anhydride	Per Cent Oil
				Alkyds—Color Retentive—Drying			
XAC 1	50	M.S.†	8 max	W-X	7.57	28	52 Soya Linseed
XAC 2	70	M.S.	9 max	V-W	7.95	23	65 Soya
XAC 5	50	Xylene	9 max	X-Z	8.30	29	33 Drying
XAC 6	70	M.S.	10 max	T-V	7.79	18	75 Drying
XAC 9	50	Xylene	7 max	$Z-Z_2$	8.29	40	37 Dehydrated castor
XAC 42	50	M.S.	9 max	Z_2-Z_4	7.60	34	50 Soya
XAC 47	70	M.S.	7 max	Z_2-Z_4	7.96	24	63 Soya
XAC 50	40	O.M.S.‡	8 max	X-Z	7.10	17	56 Soya
XAC 66	60	Xylene	11 max	Z_2-Z_4	8.40	38	45 Dehydrated castor
XAC 75	70	O.M.S.	9 max	V-W	7.78	24	67 Soya
XAC 76	65	Xylene	11 max	Y-Z	8.42	35	47 Soya
XAC 77	45	O.M.S.	8 max	$Y-Z_1$	7.25	30	57 Soya
XAC 83	70	M.S.	7 max	Z_1-Z_2	7.97	23	64 Soya
XAC 93	70	M.S.	8 max	$Y-Z_1$	8.00	24	62 Soya
XAC 99	50	M.S.	9 max	Y-Z	7.58	31	58 Soya
XAC 189	50	VM&P naphtha	9 max	V-X	7.42	30.2	56 Soya
XAC C84	60	M.S.	8 max	Z_5-Z_6	7.83	25.5	54 Drying

Alkyds—Noncolor Retentive—Drying

XAD 1	50	Xylene	11 max	W-Y	8.24	43	40 Linseed
XAD 26	50	M.S.†	10 max	U-W	7.65	33	52 Linseed
XAD 37	50	M.S.	10 max	Z_2-Z_3	7.62	35	51 Linseed
Alkyds—Nondrying							
XAN 1	60	Xylene	6 max	Z_1-Z_3	8.63	43	43 Nondrying
XAN 84	70	Toluene	6 max	V-W	8.50	33	52 Coconut
Resin Modified Alkyds							
XAR 7	50	Xylene VM&P	12 max	T-V	7.73	12.5	42 Chinawood
XAR 12	50	M.S.	11 max	X-Z	7.58	21	42 Drying
XAR 13	60	Xylene VM&P	12 max	Z_3-Z_5	8.05	30	30 Drying
XAR 19	55	Xylene VM&P	13 max	G-I	7.76	13	51 Chinawood
XAR 62	50	Xylene VM&P	12 max	T-V	7.83	30	52 Soya Chinawood
XAR C23	50	VM&P	12 max	Z-Z_2	7.68	30	30 Drying
Styrenated Alkyds							
XAS 1	50	Xylene VM&P	10 max	W-Y	7.80	22	31 Drying
XAS 4	50	Xylene	8 max	Q-T	8.07	19.7	32 Drying

* Courtesy of Sherwin-Williams Co.   † Mineral Spirits   ‡ Odorless Mineral Spirits

Commercial Alkyds

Alkyds are produced commercially in a wide range of properties. Publications of the National Paint, Varnish & Lacquer Association [1] list the physical characteristics of the majority of commercial alkyd resins.

A typical series of alkyds is shown in Table 2.2. They are divided into color-retentive drying alkyds, noncolor-retentive drying alkyds, nondrying alkyds, resin-modified alkyds, and styrenated alkyds. These alkyds can be used for a wide variety of end uses. Note that the type of solvent changes from mineral spirits to xylene when the phthalic anhydride content reaches 30 to 38 per cent. The resin solids increase from 50 per cent in the medium-oil alkyd to 70 per cent in the long-oil alkyd. The base resin in the medium-oil alkyd is more viscous than the base resin of the long-oil alkyd, so more solvent is required to reduce the resin to a pourable viscosity.

Combinations with Other Materials

One of the most remarkable properties of alkyd resins is their versatility. They can be used in combination with many other materials in order to obtain the desired properties.

Alkyds are compatible or react with other materials because of:

1. Long chain fatty acid groups which impart predominantly nonpolar characteristics to the molecule, and promotes compatibility with other nonpolar materials such as chlorinated rubber, etc.

2. Functional hydroxyl groups which can react with acid groups, amide groups, epoxy groups, etc., of other resins.

3. Functional acid groups which can react with hydroxyl groups, epoxy groups, etc.

4. Unsaturated double bonds in the fatty acid chains

which can copolymerize with unsaturated monomers such as styrene, etc.

Properties of alkyds can be upgraded in certain characteristics by using in combination with other coating materials. Much the same as GRS rubber is a combination of two materials, i.e., styrene and butadiene, alkyds are combined or blended with other materials (see Table 2.3).

TABLE 2.3

$$\text{Alkyds } \frac{\text{combined}}{\text{with}}$$

Nitrocellulose
Urea-formaldehyde resin
Melamine-formaldehyde resin
Phenolic resins
Ethyl cellulose
Chlorinated rubber
Chlorinated paraffin
Epoxy resins
Polyisocyanates
Silicone resins
Polyamides
Natural resins, rosin, congo, etc.
Cellulose acetobutyrate
Monomers—styrene, vinyl toluene,
    methyl methacrylate
Synthetic latices—styrene butadiene,
    polyvinyl acetate, acrylic

The use of oil-modified alkyds with nitrocellulose was perhaps the first merger of an alkyd with another material. The upgrading effect of the alkyd improved the gloss, adhesion, durability, and build. The combination of alkyds with urea- and melamine-formaldehyde resins produces a tough baking-type finish which is the backbone of industrial finishes. Phenolics in combination with alkyds have the excellent gloss retention and durability of alkyds plus the water and alkali resistance of the phenolics. Chlorinated rubber in combination with an alkyd produces a tough finish suitable for concrete floor paints. The addition of an epoxy

Figure 2.4. Exposure farm for evaluating exterior durability.
(*Courtesy Sherwin-Williams Co.*)

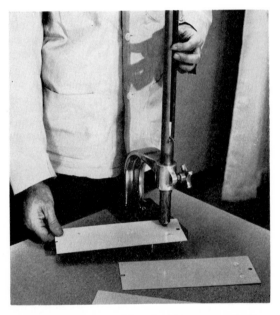

Figure 2.5. Impact tester used for alkyd coatings applied to cabinets
and appliances. (*Courtesy Sherwin-Williams Co.*)

resin to an alkyd will improve alkali resistance. Many medium- and short-oil alkyds are compatible with certain vinyl resins, and the combination of fast drying and excellent resistance is specified in a number of finishes for military use. The addition of an isocyanate to an alkyd improves adhesion and abrasion resistance. Silicone resins, which have high heat resistance but low film strength, have been combined with alkyds to produce coatings with good heat resistance. The addition of rosin to an alkyd lowers the cost and produces a vehicle with good through-drying. Styrenated alkyds, that is, alkyds in which styrene is interpolymerized with the unsaturation groups of the fatty acid, produce a "fast-drying" vehicle. Alkyds can be used in conjunction with styrene-butadiene latices and PVA latices to improve adhesion and give early washability. Alkyd polyamides produce thixotropic vehicles which are used to produce "gelled" paint. The paint is a gel until subjected to a stress such as brushing, which liquefies the paint.

Test Characteristics

There are certain characteristics determined on alkyds as control tests to insure uniformity from batch to batch and also suitability for the particular end use. Properties usually determined are specific gravity, color, acid value, nonvolatile content, and cure.

Specific gravity is determined with a hydrometer and is useful to the paint formulator in setting up formulas.

Color is measured on a Gardner Hellige Varnish Comparator. The varnish is placed in a Gardner bubble viscosity tube and compared to a series of standard colors, ranging from 1 to 18. Commercial alkyds are usually in the color range of 5 to 13. (The lower the number, the lighter the color.) Vehicles used in white and light color paints must be of minimum color.

Viscosity is measured by the use of Gardner-Holdt viscosity tubes which compare the time of an air bubble to rise in a vertical tube to that of a standard tube (see Figure 2.6). These tubes are designated in letters from A_5 to Z_{10}. Approximate viscosity in centipoises is shown in Table 2.4. Viscosity of the vehicle must be carefully controlled so as

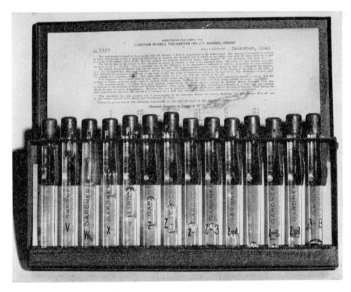

Figure 2.6. Gardner-Holdt viscosity tubes.

to produce a paint of standard viscosity. Variations in viscosity will affect the application properties of the paint whether the method is by brush, roller coat, spray, or dip. The viscosity also determines the film thickness applied in most applications.

The acid value of alkyd resins is used to follow the progress of esterification of an alkyd. As the cook progresses the polybasic acid, such as phthalic, reacts with the polyol so that the acid value drops as the reactions proceed. Also, as mentioned before, the acid value of the finished alkyd is

TABLE 2.4.   GARDNER-HOLDT VISCOSITY—CENTIPOISES.

Gardner-Holdt Bubble Tube	Poises	Gardner-Holdt Bubble Tube	Poises
A-5	0.00505	P	4.00
A-4	0.0624	Q	4.35
A-3	0.144	R	4.70
A-2	0.220	S	5.0
A-1	0.321	T	5.5
A	0.50	U	6.27
B	0.65	V	8.84
C	0.85	W	10.7
D	1.00	X	12.9
E	1.25	Y	17.6
F	1.40	Z	22.7
G	1.65	Z-1	27.0
H	2.00	Z-2	36.2
I	2.25	Z-3	46.3
J	2.50	Z-4	63.4
K	2.75	Z-5	98.5
L	3.00	Z-6	148
M	3.20	Z-7	388
N	3.40	Z-8	590
O	3.70	Z-9	855
		Z-10	1066

important from the standpoint of pigment wetting and reactivity.

Nonvolatile is a measure of the solids of the vehicle. Most alkyds when produced are dissolved in a solvent for ease of handling. Solids usually run between 30 and 90 per cent, depending on the viscosity of the base resin.

Cure is a measure of the degree of polymerization of an alkyd. Cure is determined by placing a drop of alkyd on a cure plate maintained at 200°C. The cure is measured (in seconds) from the instant of application to the instant when a manually oscillated stylus cuts a groove in the dried film. Cure is used as a means to follow the polymerization of an alkyd cook. The lower the cure, the closer is the alkyd to the gel point. Alkyds with cures below 10 sec indicate some degree of instability, so for certain applications a resin of this type cannot be used.

Reference

1. Circular 738, December 1956, Raw Material Index, Resin Section. National Paint, Varnish & Lacquer Assoc., Washington, D. C.

3. CHEMISTRY

Alkyd resins, by definition, are polymeric esters modified with fatty acids. They are prepared by the condensation of a polyhydric alcohol, a polybasic acid, and a fatty acid. This reaction, known as esterification, is one of the most elementary in organic chemistry. Although the first polymeric ester was prepared in 1847, some textbooks published as late as the 1920's stated that the polymerization of a polyester resin proceeded through an intermediate aldehyde phase. Publications of Kienle [5, 6, 7] and Carothers [2] in the late 1920's explained the polyesterification reaction in simple terms. They developed the functionality concept which shows a relation between the functionality of the reactants and the size of the molecule formed.

Functionality Concept

The functionality of the reactants determines whether a simple ester or a complex polymer is formed in the esterification reaction. By functionality is meant the number of reactive groups per molecule. Therefore, reactants such as methyl alcohol containing one hydroxyl group per mole have a functionality of one, ethylene glycol with two hydroxyl groups has a functionality of two, and glycerin with three hydroxyl groups a functionality of three, etc.

The most elementary esterification reaction is between a monofunctional acid, such as acetic acid, and a monofunctional alcohol, such as methyl alcohol, to produce methyl acetate and water (Figure 3.1A). This is a reversible reaction so that it is necessary to remove water to drive the

A. CH_3-OH + $CH_3-\overset{O}{\overset{\|}{C}}-OH$ $\rightleftharpoons$ $CH_3-\overset{O}{\overset{\|}{C}}-O-CH_3$ + H_2O

B. $HO-CH_2-CH_2-OH$ + $2CH_3-\overset{O}{\overset{\|}{C}}-OH$ $\rightleftharpoons$ $CH_3-\overset{O}{\overset{\|}{C}}-O-CH_2-CH_2-O-\overset{O}{\overset{\|}{C}}-CH_3$ + H_2O

C. $HO-\overset{O}{\overset{\|}{C}}-CH_2-CH_2-\overset{O}{\overset{\|}{C}}-OH$ + $HO-CH_2-CH_2-OH$

or

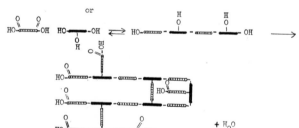

D. $HO-\overset{O}{\overset{\|}{C}}-CH_2-CH_2-\overset{O}{\overset{\|}{C}}-OH$ + $HO-CH_2-\overset{\overset{H}{\overset{|}{O}}}{\underset{}{CH}}-CH_2-OH$

or

Figure 3.1. Esterification reaction.

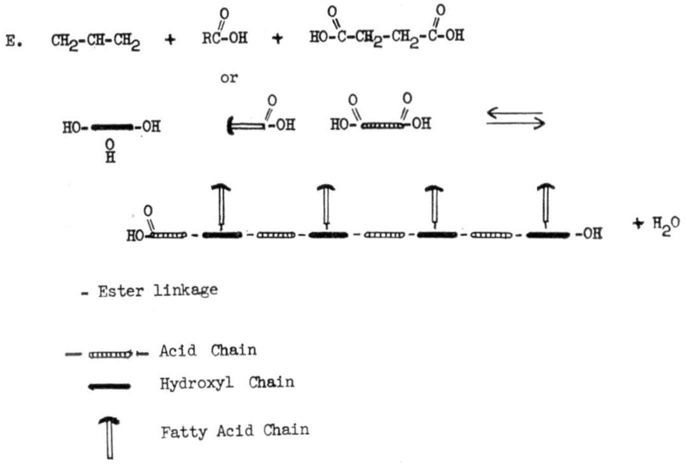

E. CH_2-CH-CH_2 + $RC\overset{O}{\overset{\|}{C}}$-OH   +   HO-$\overset{O}{\overset{\|}{C}}$-$CH_2$-$CH_2$-$\overset{O}{\overset{\|}{C}}$-OH

or

− Ester linkage

− ⊐⊐⊐⊐− Acid Chain

▬▬ Hydroxyl Chain

⊤ Fatty Acid Chain

Figure 3.1 *Cont'd.*

reaction to completion. If the methyl alcohol is now replaced with ethylene glycol, ethylene diacetate, which is a
larger molecule, is produced (Figure 3.1B).

Going one step further, by replacing acetic acid with a
bifunctional acid, such as succinic acid, a simple molecule
is no longer produced (Figure 3.1C). In the first step of
the reaction the primary ester is formed. This contains a
hydroxyl and a carboxyl end group. As the reaction progresses further, the second molecule of succinic acid can
esterify with the hydroxyl group. Then the second molecule
of ethylene glycol can esterify with the carboxyl group. This
series of reactions can continue with alternate glycol and
acid groups adding to the chain until a long linear molecule
is formed.

If the functionality of one of the reactants is greater than
two, then the course of the reaction is changed further. If
glycerin, which has a functionality of three, is reacted with

succinic acid the reaction at first is similar to the previous reaction. The succinic acid will react first with the primary hydroxyl groups of the glycerin to form short linear chains. As the reaction proceeds, the secondary hydroxyls react forming a branched structure (Figure 3.1D). Finally, branching or cross-linking proceeds to such an extent that the molecule is no longer soluble or fusible and reaches the gel state. Carothers [2] was the first to analyze this condition mathematically, and he derived a number of equations predicting the extent of the reaction at which gelation would occur. Carothers' equation is as follows:

$$P = \frac{2(No - N)}{Nof} = \frac{2\,No}{Nof} - \frac{2N}{Nof}$$

where

f = degree of functionality (average number of functional groups per molecule)

No = number of molecules at beginning of reaction

Nof = number of functional groups at beginning

N = number of molecules at end of reaction

$No - N$ = number of molecules having disappeared

$2(No - N)$ = number of functional groups lost

$$P = \text{extent of reaction} = \frac{2(No - N)}{Nof} = \frac{2No}{Nof} - \frac{2N}{Nof}$$

$$X = \text{degree of polymerization} = \frac{No}{N}$$

$$P = \frac{2}{f} - \frac{2}{Xf}; \frac{(1 \longrightarrow 0)}{X} \quad \text{therefore } P = 2/f \text{ at gel point.}$$

At gelatin, let x = infinite

then $p = \dfrac{2}{f}$

Applying the Carothers' equation to glyceryl phthalate:

	Functionality	Total
$f = \dfrac{2 \text{ moles glycerin}}{3 \text{ moles phthalic anhydride}}$	3	6
	2	6
	5	12

$p = \dfrac{2}{f} = \dfrac{2}{2.4} = 83\%$ calculated esterification.

The actual gel point of glyceryl phthalate was determined by Kienle, *et al.*[5] to be at 78.6 per cent esterification. The difference between calculated percentage and actual percentage is due to the assumption that the molecular weight at the gel point is infinite, which is not true. At the gel point the mass is not one huge single molecule but rather a large molecule enclosing many smaller ones. This has been proved by the fact that lower weight polymers can be extracted from most gels.

If a portion of the succinic acid in the above reaction is replaced with acetic acid, once again a linear polymer is formed. The acetic acid reacts with the glycerin forming a monoglyceride and leaving two hydroxyl groups which are similar to a glycol (Figure 3.1E). The succinic acid reacts with the modified glycol, forming a linear chain. These reactions have been simplified for explanation, but in actual practice, the acetic acid would react at random with the hydroxyls of the glycerin, forming a branched chain. However, the branching would not be sufficient to cause gelation.

Flory Statistical Method

Flory[3] used a statistical method to predict gelation in polyfunctional reactions. He proposed the idea of a branching index ($\propto$), which he derived by a probability theory. If a trifunctional unit is attached to a number of bifunctional units, this can lead to an infinite network only so long as chains are terminated by another trifunctional unit, since bifunctional will lead to finite molecules of definite molecular weight. Thus, the branching index ($\propto$) is the probability that a given branched unit will lead, via a series of bifunctional units, to another branched unit (see Figure 3.2).

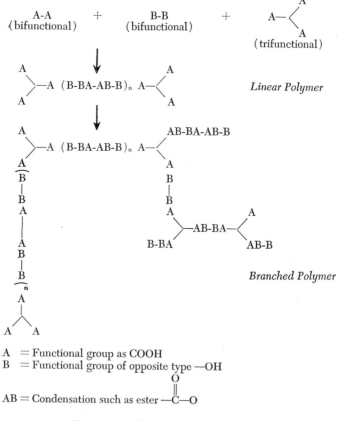

A = Functional group as COOH
B = Functional group of opposite type —OH
AB = Condensation such as ester —$\overset{\overset{\text{O}}{\|}}{\text{C}}$—O

Figure 3.2. Flory's branched chains.

Structure of Alkyds

Proceeding from simple polymeric esters to actual alkyds, the fatty acid glyceryl phthalate alkyds will be discussed first. To produce this resin the reactants used are phthalic anhydride (bifunctional), glycerin (trifunctional), and fatty acids (monofunctional). Since commercial alkyds are classified as short, medium, and long oil, depending on the amount of oil they contain, we will consider one of each type.

Figure 3.3 shows the composition and simplified structure of a short, medium, and long oil alkyd. Actually, the molecules are so complex that they cannot be drawn. They are three-dimensional, and these drawings represent only a small portion of the molecules. They do not show the branching that occurs.

Type I is an oil-free type alkyd or polyester, produced by using a large excess of hydroxyl groups. This resin is alcohol-soluble in early stages of condensation.

Type II resin is a short-oil alkyd in which fatty acid chains have reacted with a portion of the hydroxyl groups, reducing the amount of excess hydroxyl. This resin is soluble in aromatic solvents.

Type III alkyd is a medium-oil alkyd in which essentially all of the hydroxyl groups are reacted with the fatty acid chain. Such an alkyd is soluble in aliphatic-type solvents.

Type IV alkyd is a long-oil alkyd in which there is an excess of oil beyond that which will react in the molecule by esterification. The excess oil is either present but unreacted with the alkyd or bound by heat polymerization with the fatty acid in the alkyd.

Reactions Other than Esterification

The preparation of a commercial alkyd is a complex reaction and involves reactions other than esterification. Since

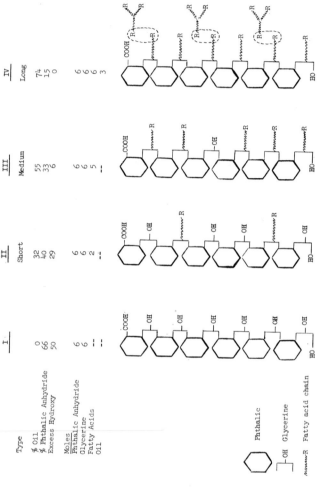

Type	I	II Short	III Medium	IV Long
% Oil	0	32	55	74
% Phthalic Anhydride	66	40	33	15
% Excess Hydroxy	50	29	6	0
Moles				
Phthalic Anhydride	6	6	6	6
Glycerine	6	6	6	6
Fatty Acids	—	2	5	6
Oil	—	—	—	3

⬡ Phthalic

⌐OH Glycerine

〜〜R Fatty acid chain

Figure 3.3. Composition of glyceryl phthalate alkyds containing various percentages of oil.

the fatty acid contains unsaturated double bonds, a certain amount of polymerization can take place during the esterification reaction (see Figure 3.4). The amount of polymerization of fatty acid is dependent on the type of oil, the time and temperature of reaction, and the amount of atmospheric oxygen which may enter the system. Investigators have reported varying amounts of oil polymerization during the alkyd reaction. R. A. Brett [1] reported that in solvent

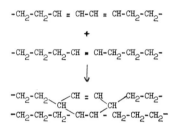

Figure 3.4. Polymerization of fatty acid chains.

cooks at 536°F about 25 per cent of the linseed oil was polymerized in a 70 per cent oil alkyd after seven hours. At 464°F only 6 per cent of the oil was polymerized in thirty hours. A comparison of the fatty acid polymerization occurring in the solvent and fusion processes showed that for the solvent process, with a 60 per cent linseed alkyd, the polymerization was 6 per cent as compared to 9 per cent for the fusion process. P. Secrest [8] reported that with soya, tall oil and linseed alkyds in solvent cooks at 400° and 450°F, little change took place in the iodine value of the oil, indicating that the amount of polymerization was nil.

It may seem uneconomic to split a vegetable oil into fatty acids and glycerin, and then recombine these materials into an alkyd. In some cases the fatty acids are obtained from other sources such as tall oil, and the glycerin by a synthetic process from petroleum. However, if an attempt is made to prepare an alkyd by reacting phthalic anhydride, glycerin, and a vegetable oil together as the glyceryl phthalate forms it would precipitate and be insoluble in the oil. An alkyd can be prepared from these ingredients if the reaction is carried out in a slightly different manner. The oil is first converted to a monoglyceride by heating with a polyalcohol in the presence of a catalyst. The monoglyceride is then reacted with phthalic anhydride to form the alkyd (Figure 3.5).

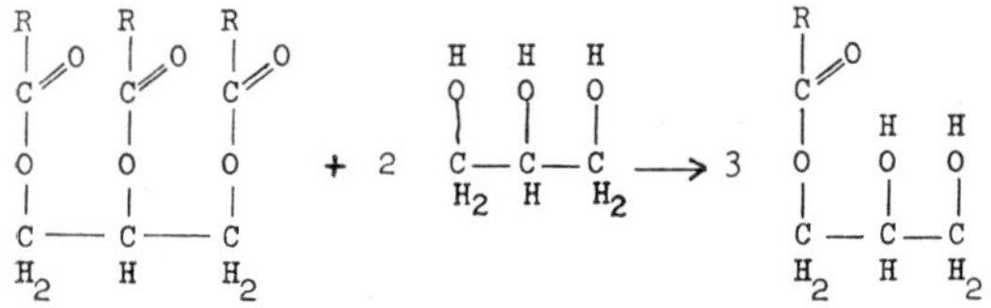

Figure 3.5. Alcoholysis.

Another method of preparing an alkyd directly from an oil is called acidolysis. In this procedure the oil is heated with a dibasic acid, such as phthalic, which displaces some of the fatty acid in the triglyceride, then the polyol is added to form the alkyd (see Figure 3.6).

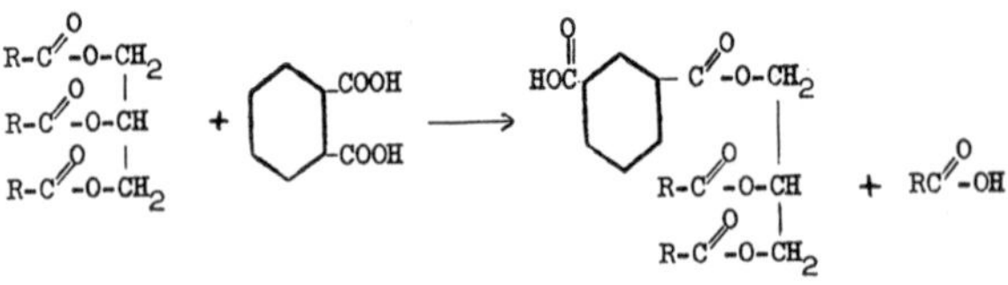

Figure 3.6. Acidolysis.

Other reactions, such as etherification of the alcoholic hydroxyl groups, may occur during the manufacture of alkyd resins. An excess of water collected during the reaction over the water of esterification suggests etherification.

Water would be evolved from the reaction without a reduction in acid value (Figure 3.7). Etherification is most likely to occur during the alcoholysis stage when an excess of polyhydric alcohol is present with an alkaline catalyst. Very little etherification takes place in the subsequent esterification reaction. Certain polyols, such as sorbitol, are more prone to form ethers. Commercial pentaerythritol contains

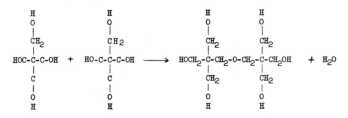

Figure 3.7. Etherification.

a small percentage of ether groups in dipentaerythritol at the start.

From the multiple reactions which can take place in an alkyd cook, it is evident that the final alkyd molecule is a very complex polymer. Under various reaction conditions different end products are formed.

References

1. Brett, R. A., *J. Oil & Colour Chemists' Assoc.*, **41**, 428-52 (1958).
2. Carothers, W. H., *Trans. Faraday Soc.*, **32**, 39 (1936).
3. Flory, P. J., *J. Am. Chem. Soc.*, **63**, 3083 (1941).
4. Flory, P. J., *Chem. Rev.*, **39**, 137 (1946).
5. Kienle, R. H., van der Mueller, P. A., Petke, F. E., *J. Am. Chem. Soc.*, **61**, 2258-68 (1939).
6. Kienle, R. H., Petke, F. E., *J. Am. Chem. Soc.*, **62**, 1053 (1940).
7. Kienle, R. H., Petke, F. E., *J. Am. Chem. Soc.*, **63**, 481 (1941).
8. Secrest, P. J., "Changes in Iodine Value and Refractive Index of Fatty Acids During Alkyd Resin Manufacture and Analysis" presented to American Oil Chemists' Society, Dallas, 1960.

4. RAW MATERIALS

Theoretically, any organic acid or alcohol could be used in alkyd resins. Actually, relatively few have the physical, chemical and economical properties for use in alkyd resins. Vegetable oils and fatty acids are natural products and many types are used. Here, again, economics is a factor and in certain geographical areas it may be advantageous to use certain oils. The market prices of vegetable oils vary in relation to each other so that sometimes it may be advantageous to use one oil in place of another. Figure 4.1 shows prices of several oils for the past twenty years.

Oils

Oil imparts flexibility to an alkyd film. In the case of coconut oil, which is nondrying, there is no further change in an alkyd. Where a drying oil such as linseed is used in an alkyd, the solvent first evaporates and then the unsaturated double bonds polymerize further by atmospheric oxidation. In general, the greater the unsaturation, as measured by the iodine value, the greater is the drying phenomenon and usually the darker the color of the alkyd. Fatty oils are triglycerides of alpihatic acids having 18 carbons in their chain. The number of unsaturated double bonds varies from stearic acid, which is completely saturated and therefore has no double bonds, to eleostearic acid which has three conjugated double bonds. Natural oils contain varying amounts of these fatty acids. Average composition of natural oils is shown in Table 4.1. Composition varies slightly from year to year, depending on natural conditions.

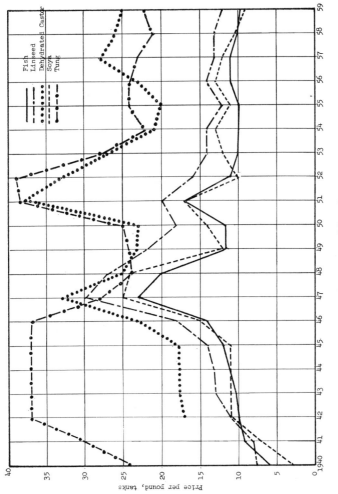

Figure 4.1. Vegetable oil prices.

TABLE 4.1. COMPARISON OF VEGETABLE AND MARINE DRYING OILS.*

	Linseed Oil, Raw	Raw Castor Oil	Dehydrated Castor Oil	Oiticica Oil	Tung Oil	Soya Bean Oil	Safflower Oil	Crude Tall Oil	Fish Oil
Acid no.	2-4	5-12	3-6	3-8	—	0.5-6.0	1-4	165-170	0.5-8.0
Sap. no.	188-196	172-182	188-194	185-195	190-195	189-195	188-194	170-180	185-195
Sp. gr.	0.931-0.934	0.963	0.938-0.941	0.973	0.940-0.942	0.924	0.924	0.960-0.984	0.923-0.933
Wt/gal	7.76	8.08	7.81	8.10	7.85	7.70	7.70	8.11	7.73-7.78
Iodine no.	170-190	85	125-140	145-165	160-165	130-140	145	143-170	165-195
Color	11-12	8-9	4-6	8-11	9-12	9.5-10.5	10-10.5	10-dark	12-14
Viscosity	A	U	G-H	W-X	H-J	A	A	S-V	A
Sat. acids	5.0	2.0	2.0	12.5	5.5	13.2	6.6	7	20
Oleic	5.0	8.6	8.6	4.5	15.0	30.2	16.4	16-25	10
9-12 Linoleic	40.0	3.5	57.0	—	—	51.2	76.7	16-25	15
9-11 Linoleic	—	—	25.5	—	—	—	—	—	—
Linolenic	50.0	—	—	—	—	5.4	0.3	—	—
Licanic	—	—	—	83.0	—	—	—	—	—
Ricinoleic	—	85.9	6.9	—	—	—	—	—	—
Eleostearic	—	—	—	—	79.5	—	—	—	—
Refractive index	1.4775	—	1.4873	1.5100-1.5160	1.5160-1.5200	1.4734-1.4740	—	—	—
Arachidonic	—	—	—	—	—	—	—	—	30
Clupanodonic	—	—	—	—	—	—	—	—	25
Rosinacids	—	—	—	—	—	—	—	42-51	—

* Courtesy *Paint Industry Magazine*.[2]

The oils most commonly used are:

Linseed Oil. Linseed is derived from flaxseed which contains about 35 per cent oil. Linseed oil has the largest usage of any oil in the protective coatings field. It is used in alkyds as well as in oleoresinous varnishes and as the sole vehicle in exterior house paints. Linseed oil has good drying properties but has a tendency to yellow.

Soya Oil. Soybean oil is an edible oil, a large proportion of which is used in food products. It is obtained from soy beans which contain about 20 per cent oil. For coating purposes, soya oil is classified as a semidrying oil. Its primary use in the protective coatings field is in alkyds, where it has good color retention properties.

Dehydrated Castor Oil. Castor beans are grown principally in Brazil although there is some cultivation in the United States. Castor oil, itself, is a nondrying oil containing hydroxyl groups which can be dehydrated catalytically to form a drying oil. Dehydrated castor oil is an improvement over linseed oil in many respects such as drying properties, non-yellowing, and bodying rate. It approaches tung oil in such properties as drying, and water and alkali resistance.

Tung Oil. Most of the tung oil used in this country up until a few years ago was imported from China, hence the name Chinawood oil. However, because of political conditions, tung trees have been cultivated in the south. In 1958 over half the tung oil used in this country was domestic. Tung oil, which is produced from the nut of the tung tree, is the fastest drying, the hardest and most water resistant of any natural drying oil.

Safflower Oil. The oil from safflower seeds, which are grown in the western part of the United States, first appeared on the American market in 1949. Safflower oil has most of the desirable properties of linseed and soya oils combined in a single oil.

Oiticica Oil. Oiticica oil, obtained from the nut of the oiticica tree, is imported from Brazil. Its performance is close to tung oil in many respects.

Fish Oil. Very little fish oil (sardine and menhaden) is used in alkyds because of its odor and variation in characteristics, depending on the source.

Tall Oil. Tall oil, which is actually a mixture of rosin and fatty acids, is obtained as a by-product of the Kraft process for making wood pulp. Tall oil can be refined by distillation and other methods so that it can be used in alkyds. It has semidrying characteristics, and its properties depend to a large extent on the refinement.

Cottonseed Oil and Coconut Oil. These are nondrying oils and are used in baking-type or plasticizing-type alkyds. They have good color retention properties.

Synthetic Nondrying Fatty Acids. There are many new synthetic nondrying fatty acids such as pelargonic, isodecanoic, and isooctanoic which are now being used to produce improved nondrying alkyds.

Acids and Anhydrides (See Table 4.2).

These materials are used either in the acid or, in some cases, in the anhydride form. The anhydride is formed from two equivalents of acid minus a mole of water. Reaction rates are more rapid when the anhydride is used and there is consequently less water to be removed from the reaction. Not all organic acids are available as anhydrides, as this is dependent on molecular structure.

The most commonly used dibasic acid is phthalic anhydride. Other aliphatic and aromatic acids are used to obtain specific properties in an alkyd.

Phthalic Acid and Anhydride. Phthalic anhydride is the principal dibasic acid used in alkyds. Unless otherwise stated, phthalic refers to the *ortho* form. This is produced by

TABLE 4.2. ACIDS AND ANHYDRIDES.

Name	Form	Molecular Weight	Melting Point °F	Boiling Point °F
Phthalic anhydride (*ortho*)	White solid	148.11	270	544
Phthalic acid (*ortho*)	White solid	166.13	375-410 Decomposes	Decomposes
Isophthalic acid (*meta*)	White needles	166.13	650	Sublimes
Terephthalic acid (*para*)	White crystals	166.13	Sublimes > 570	—
Tetrahydrophthalic acid	White solid	170.16	248	—
Hexahydrophthalic acid	White solid	172.18	377	—
Benzoic acid	White solid	122.12	251	482
Maleic anhydride	White solid	98.06	126	395
Maleic acid	White solid	116.07	266	275
Fumaric acid	White solid	116.07	548	554
Succinic anhydride	White solid	100.07	248	502
Adipic acid	White solid	146.14	306	509
Sebacic acid	White solid	202.25	271	563 @ 100 min

the catalytic oxidation of naphthalene and, to a lesser extent, orthoxylene.

Isophthalic acid has become available commercially in the past few years. It is produced from petroleum sources, i.e., by the catalytic oxidation of various xylenes. Isophthalic acid, which cannot be obtained as an anhydride, is in the *meta* form.

Terephthalic acid is the *para* form of the acid and finds its principal use in materials for fibers.

Tetrahydrophthalic, Hexahydrophthalic and Nadic * Anhydride. A series of special phthalic anhydrides which are produced commercially from the Diels-Alder reaction of maleic anhydride with butadiene, cyclopentadiene and other unsaturated petroleum products. Because of their higher cost they have found only limited use in alkyds.

Maleic Anhydride and Acid. Maleic anhydride is obtained from the catalytic oxidation of naphthalene and is the *cis*-form of butendioic anhydride. Maleic anhydride or acid is an unsaturated acid and the double bonds will therefore cross-link with the double bonds of the fatty acids. Since this increases the functionality of the system it is sometimes added to alkyds to increase viscosity.

Fumaric Acid. Fumaric acid is the *trans*-form of maleic acid. One method of commercial production is by fermentation.

Adipic Acid. Adipic acid is obtained from the oxidation of cyclohexane. Adipic acid is used as an ingredient in nylon and in polyester resins. When used in an alkyd, this material produces a softer or more flexible resin.

Benzoic Acid. Benzoic acid cannot be used as the sole organic acid in an alkyd. However, if a small amount of phthalic anhydride is replaced with benzoic acid, this acts as a "chain stopper" and the alkyd can be cooked to lower acid values without gelation.

Alcohols

Many different polyols [1] are used in alkyds, the most common of which is glycerin. If the alcoholysis method is used to produce an alkyd, glycerin is of course part of the composition of the oil portion as the fatty acids are triglycerides. A list of polyols used in alkyds is shown in Table 4.3.

* Trade name, National Aniline.

TABLE 4.3. POLYOLS.

Name	Formula	Form	Molecular Weight	Boiling Point, °F
Ethylene glycol	H HC–OH | HC–OH H	Liquid	62.07	386
Diethylene glycol	H H H H HO–C–C–O–C–C–OH H H H H	Liquid	106.12	473
Propylene glycol	H H H HC–C–C–OH H | H O H	Liquid	76.09	374
Glycerin CP-95% glycerin Super-98% glycerin	H HC–OH | HC–OH | HC–OH H	Liquid	92.09	554

Name	Formula	Form	Molecular Weight	Melting Point, °F
Trimethylol ethane	CH_2OH | CH_3–C–CH_2OH | CH_2OH	White solid	120.15	395
Trimethylol propane	CH_2OH | C_2H_5–C–CH_2OH | CH_2OH	White solid	134.18	136
Pentaerythritol	$HOCH_2$ H_2C–OH \\ / C / \\ $HOCH_2$ H_2C–OH	White solid	136.15	504

TABLE 4.3. POLYOLS. *Cont'd*

Name	Formula	Form	Molecular Weight	Boiling Point, °F
Sorbitol	CH₂OH │ HC-OH │ HO-CH │ HC-OH │ HC-OH │ CH₂OH	White solid	182.17	195-230

Glycerin. Glycerin was first obtained as a by-product of the splitting of fats and oils in the manufacture of soap. In the early 1940's glycerin was first produced commercially from petroleum sources. This synthetic production stabilized the price of glycerin. Glycerin has a functionality of three and it is, therefore, possible to carry the alkyd reaction to a specific point and have a lower viscosity than with polyols of higher functionality. Glycerin contains both primary and secondary alcohol groups with secondary groups having slower reactivity. The principal use of glycerin is in short- and medium-oil alkyds. Glycerin is used in many alkyds for the following reasons:

(1) In the liquid state it is easy to handle in production.
(2) Because of its high boiling point it can be used in either fusion or solvent cooks.
(3) There is ample supply at a reasonable price.
(4) Glycerin alkyds have excellent solubility and compatibility properties.
(5) Glycerin alkyds have good film properties.

Pentaerythritol. Pentaerythritol, a polyol second only to glycerin in alkyd usage, is produced by the condensation of acetaldehyde with formaldehyde in an aqueous alkaline medium. Pentaerythritol contains four primary hydroxyl groups. Pentaerythritol alkyds are noted for:

1. Good brushability
2. Improved drying and hardness
3. Good color stability upon exposure to heat and light
4. Excellent durability
5. Excellent gloss retention

Pentaerythritol is an outstanding polyol for use in long-oil alkyds.

Polypentaerythritol. Dipentaerythritol and tripentaerythritol are both by-products of pentaerythritol manufacture. Because of their high functionality, six and eight respectively, their use is chiefly in long-oil alkyds.

Ethylene Glycol. Ethylene glycol is the most important glycol in alkyd resins. Glycols are the lowest cost polyols available for use in alkyds. Their volatility is a disadvantage in alkyd manufacture. In many cases glycols are combined with polyols of higher functionality such as pentaerythritol.

Trimethylolethane. Trimethylolethane, one of the newer polyols, is made by the condensation of formaldehyde with propionaldehyde. While trimethylolethane in alkyds shows some advantages over other polyols, acceptance has been slow because of its higher price.

Trimethylolpropane. Produced from the condensation of formaldehyde with butyraldehyde. Trimethylolpropane has been produced in volume for many years in Germany for use in polyurethane resins. Trimethylolpropane alkyds are slightly softer than comparable trimethylolethane alkyds.

Sorbitol. Sorbitol is produced by the catalytic hydrogenation of glucose, and although it has been available commercially for some twenty years it has found very little use in alkyds. Even though sorbitol contains six hydroxyl groups, its functionality is usually calculated as four since not all the hydroxyls will esterify under alkyd-processing conditions.

References

1. Barr, N. P., Boden, V. H., Hall, T. J., Burns, J. P., Gibbons, J. P., Kraft, W. M., and Vaughan, C. L. P., *Paint Varnish Production,* **48,** 44-73 (October 1958).
2. Farber, B., Glaser, D. W., Goodkin, S. J., Paulkner, O., Smallwood, B., and Roberts, G. T., *Paint Ind. Mag.,* **75,** 10-28 (June 1960).

5. ALKYD CALCULATIONS

An alkyd resin is a polymer produced by combining a di-functional acid, a polyfunctional alcohol, and a fatty acid or oil. The proportions of materials and process conditions must be correct or the resultant polymer will gel during the cooking process.

Functionality

Theories of condensation polymerization set forth by Carothers and Kienle conclude that the average over-all functionality for a useful film-forming alkyd resin should be

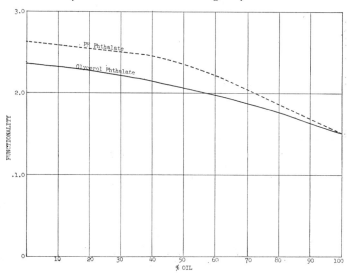

Figure 5.1. Functionality of alkyds using molar equivalents.

about two. Then in cooking, the esterification is stopped just short of completion before the gel point is reached.

The combination of a difunctional acid and a difunctional polyol will give a finished composition with a functionality of two. The correct proportion of a difunctional acid, a tri- or tetra-functional alcohol, and a monobasic acid, such as a fatty acid, will also give a composition with a functionality of two.

TABLE 5.1. CALCULATION OF FUNCTIONALITY OF AN ALKYD.

Example 1: 60% Oil Alkyd

	Moles	Functionality	f x m
Phthalic anhydride	1.0	2.0	2.0
Glycerin	1.0	3.0	3.0
Soya fatty acids	1.0	1.0	1.0
	3.0		6.0

Excess hydroxyl   0%

Functionality $\dfrac{6.0}{3.0} = 2.0$

Example 2: 43% Oil Alkyd

	Moles	Functionality	f x m
Phthalic anhydride	1.0	2.0	2.0
Glycerin	1.0	2.5 [a]	2.5
Soya fatty acids	0.5	1.0	0.5
	2.5		5.0

Excess hydroxyl   20%

(a) Functionality of glycerin: $f = \dfrac{3}{1 + 0.20} = 2.5$

Functionality of system: $f = \dfrac{5.0}{2.5} = 2.0$

Therefore, if an alkyd were formulated on the basis of molar equivalents, as the oil length increases the functionality decreases due to the increase in the amount of monofunctional material, i.e., fatty acids. Figure 5.1 shows a glycerin phthalic alkyd formulated on the basis of molar equivalents, i.e., there are equal equivalents of acid and alcohol so that the excess hydroxyl content is zero per cent. From this curve we see that the functionality varies from 2.4 in the case of the alkyd containing no oil to 1.5 at 100 per cent oil. On this same curve is also shown pentaerythritol alkyds which have higher functionality.

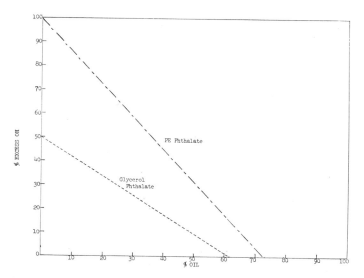

Figure 5.2. Variation in excess hydroxyl in alkyds formulated to a functionality of two.

Since a composition with a functionality much over two will cross-link or gel long before the esterification reaction is complete, it is necessary in the case of shorter oil alkyds to reduce the functionality of the over-all composition by increasing the amount of polyol present. For example, if glycerin has a normal functionality of three, a 50 per cent excess (over phthalic anhydride) must be used to reduce functionality to 2.0. In Table 5.1 examples are shown of the calculation of the functionality of an alkyd. In both cases the alkyds have a functionality of 2.0.

If a series of glyceryl phthalate alkyds is calculated over a range of oil lengths, the per cent of excess hydroxyl will vary from zero to 50 per cent, as shown in Figure 5.2. On this same curve are shown pentaerythritol alkyds. Because of the higher functionality of pentaerythritol it is seldom used as the sole polyol in a low-oil-content alkyd.

Composition

There are certain terms used to describe or compare the composition of alkyds. These are phthalic anhydride content, glyceryl phthalate content, per cent fatty acids, per cent oil, etc.

Phthalic Anhydride. Minimum phthalic anhydride content is incorporated in many specifications. This is calculated as follows:

$$\text{Theoretical phthalic anhydride} = \frac{100 \times (\text{phthalic anhydride input})}{(\text{total base input}) - (\text{water loss})}$$

The actual per cent phthalic anhydride found by analysis is usually 1 to 2 per cent less than the theoretical.

Glyceryl Phthalate Content.

$$\text{Glyceryl phthalate content} = 1.29 \times (\text{phthalic anhydride content})$$

Per Cent Fatty Acids and Oil.

$$\text{Per cent fatty acid} = \frac{\text{Fatty acids}}{\text{Base input} - \text{water}}$$

$$\text{Per cent oil} = 1.04 \times (\text{per cent fatty acids})$$

TABLE 5.2. EQUIVALENT WEIGHTS.

	Equivalent Weight
Polybasic Acids and Anhydrides	
Adipic acid	73
Fumaric acid	58
Isophthalic acid	83
Maleic anhydride	49
Phthalic anhydride	74

TABLE 5.2. EQUIVALENT WEIGHTS.

	Equivalent Weight
Polyhydric Alcohols	
Ethylene glycol	31
Diethylene glycol	53
Glycerin (99%)	31
Pentaerythritol	34
Dipentaerythritol	43
Trimethylolethane	40
Trimethylolpropane	45

Equivalent weights of polyols can be calculated from the hydroxyl content.

$$\text{Equivalent weight} = \frac{17 \times 100}{\% \text{ OH}}$$

Fatty Acids and Oils	
Coconut F. A.	215
Cottonseed F.A.	282
Dehydrated castor F.A.	285
Linseed F.A.	280
Soya bean F.A.	280
Tall oil F.A.	285
Castor oil	310
Coconut oil	229
Cottonseed oil	293
Dehydrated castor oil	293
Linseed oil	293
Safflower oil	293
Soybean oil	293
Tung oil	293

Equivalent weights of fatty acids are calculated from their analytical acid value and vary from different sources.

$$\text{Equivalent weight} = \frac{56,100}{\text{acid number}}$$

Equivalent weight of oils signifies one equivalent of fatty acid and one equivalent of glycerin.

Miscellaneous Materials	
Rosin	340
Benzoic acid	122
Abitol *	350

* Trade-mark, Hercules Powder Co., Inc.

Calculation

Shown below are examples of calculations of a fatty acid alkyd formula and an alcoholysis formula:

Fatty Acid

Composition	Equivalents COOH	Equivalents OH	Grams	% in final alkyd
Soya fatty acids	1.200	—	336	58.0
Pentaerythritol	—	3.84	131	23.0
Phthalic anhydride	2.00	—	148	26.0
	3.20	3.84	615	107.0
		Water loss	40	−7.0
			575	100.0

1. Excess hydroxyl $= \dfrac{100(3.84\text{-}3.20)}{3.20} = 20\%$

2. Theoretical phthalic anhydride $= \dfrac{100(148)}{(575)} = 25\%$

3. Fatty acids $= \dfrac{100(336)}{(575)} = 58\%$

4. Oil $= (1.04)(58\%) = 60\%$

Alcoholysis

Linseed oil	.50	.50	148	42.0
Glycerin	—	2.40	74	21.0
Phthalic anhydride	2.00	—	148	42.0
	2.50	2.90	370	105.0
		Water loss	18	−5.0
			352	100.0

1. Excess hydroxyl $= \dfrac{100(2.90\text{-}2.50)}{2.50} = 16\%$

2. Theoretical phthalic anhydride $= \dfrac{100(42)}{105} = 40\%$

3. Glyceryl phthalate $= \dfrac{100(148\text{-}74\text{-}18)}{352} = 57\%$

4. Oil $= \dfrac{100(148)}{352} = 42\%$

Reference

1. Vaughn, C. L. P., and Schmitt, F. E. Jr., *Offic. Dig.*, **30**, No. 405, 1131 (1958).

6. MANUFACTURE

Alkyd resins are produced by a two-step batch process. The first step is the esterification reaction in which the materials are reacted to a specified end point. Then the resin is partially cooled and dropped into solvent in the thinning tank. From this point the alkyd is pumped to filter presses for clarification and then to storage tanks. Alkyds are produced in equipment that will yield from 100 to 10,000 gallons, depending on size. Continuous methods of producing alkyds are described in the literature,[1] however, they have not been adopted. Since there are innumerable different alkyds produced, the batch process will continue to be used.

The esterification reaction can be carried out by one of two general methods—fusion process or solvent process.

Fusion Process. In the fusion method the reactants are charged into the kettle and heated under an inert gas atmosphere. Near the end of the cook, inert gas is blown into the resin mass to carry off water and unreacted materials. Advantages of the fusion process are:

1. Lower equipment investment
2. Less fire hazard

Solvent Process. The solvent process uses a small amount of solvent, 5 to 10 per cent, in the reaction to act as a reflux medium. The water of reaction is carried off by the solvent, separated out, and the solvent returned to the batch. Advantages of the solvent process are:

1. Lower raw material losses
2. Lighter color product
3. Easier clean-up of kettle

The reaction temperature can be controlled by the type and amount of solvent added. The solvent used must have a Kauri Butanol solvency of at least 70 in order to dissolve the phthalic anhydride.

Solvent	Per Cent	Reflux Temperature °F
Xylene	3	485-500
Xylene	4	475-485
Xylene	7	400-410
High-flash naphtha	10	400-410

In plant operation, reflux temperature is controlled by adding or withdrawing solvent.

Reaction Kettle

The reaction kettles are similar to batch reactor equipment used in the chemical industry. Kettles are fitted with an agitator, a manhole, lines to charge liquid reactants, condensers, temperature-measuring devices, sampling devices, a discharge line and a source of heat (see Figure 6.1).

Materials of Construction. Corrosion-resistant materials must be used since any contamination of the resin will affect the color as well as other properties. For this reason and because of its long service life, stainless steel or stainless steel-clad equipment has become standard in the industry. Kettles are cleaned with caustic periodically; stainless steel equipment is not harmed by this treatment. Surfaces should be polished for ease of cleaning.

Manhole or Charging Port. The manhole is used for charging solid raw materials. It is also used for access to the kettle for cleaning and repairs.

Heat Exchange System. Alkyd kettles can be heated by direct fire, electrical or Dowtherm heating. Steam cannot

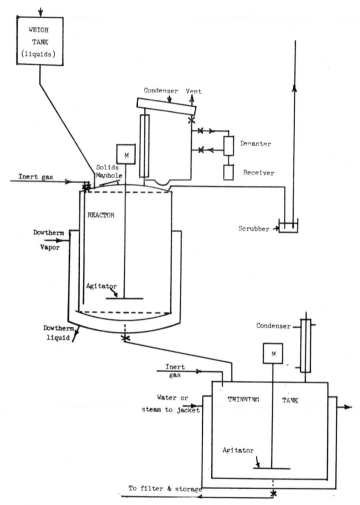

Figure 6.1. Typical equipment used for alkyd manufacture.

be used as temperatures up to 500°F must be attained. Thermal efficiency of these systems is as follows:

Dowtherm	55-65%
Electricity	75-90%
Gas	50-65%
Oil	35-50%

Direct firing is the lowest cost method of heating and has the fastest rate of heat-up. Direct firing has a disadvantage in that there is a tendency toward local overheating. This chars materials on the bottom of the kettle thereby affecting the color of the resin. In direct-fired units, gas or oil is commonly used for fuel.

Electrical heating has overcome the problem of local overheating but the initial cost of installation is high. Also, except in certain areas where electrical power is cheap, the cost of operation is high.

Dowtherm vapor heating has been used to an increasing extent since 1940. Dowtherm vapor functions in the same way as steam when introduced into a jacketed kettle. The vapor gives off its latent heat to the batch as it is condensed, and the condensate is returned to the boiler. Dowtherm can be used as a liquid transfer medium up to a temperature of 500°F, which is its boiling point. Dowtherm is stable up to temperatures of 700°F but it is usually not necessary or desirable to operate at temperatures over 600°F and pressures of 40 psi. Dowtherm heating offers the advantage of rapid cooling, if required, by the circulation of cold Dowtherm liquid through the jacket.

Cooling Equipment. There is a need for cooling equipment at the end of the cook to stop the reaction. It is advantageous to cool the resin as rapidly as possible from temperatures of ±450° to ±300°F before dropping into solvent. As mentioned before, in a Dowtherm system this is

Figure 6.2. Alkyd kettle. (*Courtesy Brighton Corporation*)

accomplished by circulating cold liquid Dowtherm through the jacket. In other systems cold fingers or cooling coils are installed in the kettle and a coolant passed through.

Agitation. Agitation serves a dual purpose—first, to maintain intimate mixing of the reactants to give satisfactory reaction rates and, second, to provide sufficient agitation to give good heat transfer through the walls of the reactor. It has been found that turbine-type agitators give the best results. Efficient agitation should revolve material around the kettle thirty to sixty times a minute. If foaming is likely to occur, the agitator should be fitted with a foam breaker. The agitators must be driven by sufficient power to handle viscous materials without splashing.

Vapor Outlets and Condensers. In the production of alkyd resin, water is evolved from the reaction and must be removed from the kettle in order that the reaction can proceed to completion. However, the water vapor carries over other materials, such as phthalic anhydride and fatty acids, so that the vapors must be passed through a scrubber before discharging into the atmosphere. A reflux condenser is desirable for the more efficient utilization of glycols, which may form azeotropic mixtures with water and thus distill out of the kettle. After the glycol has been partially esterified in the early part of the cook, the condensers can be shut off.

A condenser must be used in a solvent cook to recycle the solvent. In production of styrenated alkyds, since styrene is a volatile monomer, a condenser is needed to confine the styrene to the kettle.

An inert gas blanket is used to protect the resin during cooking. Air, or specifically, the oxygen in the air, will cause darkening in color and gelation if in contact with the resin. Carbon dioxide or nitrogen from cylinders is used for this purpose. Inert gas can be produced from the partial combustion of natural gas, coke, etc. Composition of such a gas is about 87 per cent nitrogen and 13 per cent carbon dioxide.

Thinning Tanks. After the alkyd has been esterified to the desired end point it is partially cooled and dropped into solvent. The tank used for this purpose is water cooled, fitted with a condenser and an agitator, and mounted on scales so that it is possible to add the exact amount of solvent desired. Since most alkyds are thinned to 50 per cent solids,

Figure 6.3. Thinning tanks. (*Courtesy Sherwin-Williams Co.*)

the thinning tank is usually at least twice the capacity of the reactor.

Filtering Equipment. Manufactured alkyds sometimes contain gel particles and other suspended matter, so they are filtered to remove these materials. Usually a plate-and-frame filter press or other type equipment can be used for this purpose.

Figure 6.4. Storage tanks for alkyds and other paint vehicles. (*Courtesy Sherwin-Williams Co.*)

(Left) Maleic anhydride   (Right) Phthalic anhydride

Figure 6.5. Raw materials in briquette and pellet form for ease of handling and reduction of dust.

Manufacturing Procedure

The raw materials used are both liquid and solid and are brought to the manufacturing area in tanks, drums, bags and other containers. Liquids such as oils, glycerin, etc., are pumped from the storage tanks into the weighing tank to be weighed and then introduced into the batch. Dry materials are charged into the kettle through a manhole from drums or bags. It is desirable to have solid materials in pellet or briquette form so that there will be a minimum of dust, and yet material will dissolve quickly in the batch. In most alkyd reactions all the materials are not added at the beginning. The batch is being constantly sampled and tested during the cook and when the proper point is reached, additional raw materials are added. Characteristics being checked during the cook are usually cure, viscosity, and acid value. When the proper end point is reached the reaction is terminated by cooling and dropping into solvent.

References

1. Haines, E. C. (to E. G. Wetherill Varnish Co., Inc.), U. S. Patent 2,396,698 (June 6, 1944).
2. Yokell, S., *Paint Varnish Production,* **44,** No. 3, 25 (1954).
3. Yokell, S., *Paint Varnish Production,* **43,** No. 8, 21-24 (1953).
4. Yokell, S., *Paint Varnish Production,* **42,** No. 8, 23 (1952).
5. Anon., "Dowtherm Heat Transfer," *Paint Varnish Production,* **49,** No. 7, 53 (1959).
6. Philip, J., *Paint Manuf.,* **23,** 410 (1953).
7. Hovey, A. G., *Ind. Eng. Chem.,* **41,** 730 (1949).
8. "The Chemistry and Processing of Alkyd Resins," Monsanto Chemical Co., 1952.

7. POLYMER PROPERTIES

Alkyd resins are very complex polymers and while many attempts have been made to examine them, there are still many facets to be explored. Esterification is the principal reaction taking place in the preparation of an alkyd; however, there are other reactions such as polymerization of the oil, etherification, etc., which occur and complicate the reaction. Alkyds are a mixture of polymers of varying molecular weights which also complicates the picture.

Many investigators in the United States and England have examined specific alkyds in an effort to determine the relationship between composition, molecular weight distribution, viscosity behavior, molecular structure and other properties. Findings of some of these investigators are as follows.

Structure of Alkyds

R. A. Brett [4] studied many factors of alkyd architecture. He found that in a 70 per cent oil-length linseed glyceryl alkyd some 25 per cent of the original fatty acids will be polymerized. In contrast, a similar pentaerythritol alkyd had only half as much of the fatty acids polymerized. The polymerization of fatty acids in alkyd manufacture occurs at the same temperature as in simple oil bodying. Thus, at 280°C some seven hours are required to polymerize about a quarter of the original fatty acids in a long linseed alkyd whereas at 240°C polymerization is very slow, only 6 per cent of the polymeric acids being formed in 30 hours. Both of these figures relate to the solvent process. A comparison of the fatty acid polymerization occurring in solvent and fusion processes showed that in a given heat treatment the effect was less for the solvent process; 6 per cent as compared to 9 per cent in a 60 per cent linseed alkyd. It was found that under certain conditions as much as 27 per cent of the glycerin etherifies to form diglycerol. Hydrogen bonding was also measured by these investigators. Since alkyd resins contain both hydroxyl and carboxyl groups it is not surprising that hydrogen bonding can occur. This can be shown by treating the alkyd with diazomethane and acetic anhydride to reduce the number of free carboxyl and free hydroxyl groups. The viscosity of the treated alkyd is reduced appreciably. These investigators also found that solvent extraction with various solvents extracted various types of materials. With polar solvents such as alcohols, low-molecular-weight materials high in hydroxyl content were removed thereby improving the drying and other properties of the remaining materials. Extraction with nonpolar solvents such as petroleum ether also removed low-molecular-weight materials.

A study of two 70 per cent linseed oil alkyds, one produced by the alcoholysis method and the other from fatty acids, showed equal polymerized fatty acids content. However, the amount of material extracted with petroleum ether from the monoglyceride-produced material was greater, indicating a lower molecular weight resin. The relation between solubility in petroleum ether and linear structure of the alkyd has also been studied.

Phase Separation

A. J. Seavell [14] used low-temperature-phase separation to examine several alkyds. Acetone was used as the solvent and various portions of the alkyd separated by dropping temperature in steps down to −65°C. The portions separated out first were of higher molecular weight, lower acid value, higher phthalic anhydride content, and faster drying than the more soluble material. The mean molecular weight of the first portions was about 35,000 to 39,000 while the lower fractions had a mean molecular weight of 17,000 to 24,000. Also, phase separations of similar alkyds made by both fusion and solvent processes showed that more uniform molecular weight materials were obtained by solvent cooking.

A. R. H. Tawn [16] made a study of saturated alkyds using both chromatography and fractional precipitation from dilute solutions to show the wide variation in polymers present in commercial alkyds.

T. R. Bullett and A. T. S. Rudran [5] reported on polymer structure and film formation of various vehicles including alkyds. The oxygen uptake of various alkyds was reported. Solvent extractions of a 70 per cent oil length alkyd with isopropanol showed that the extracted portion was of low molecular weight, high in hydroxyl content, and slow drying.

Viscosity-Solubility Relationships

The solubility of paint resins in hydrocarbon solvents was studied by W. W. Reynolds.[12] He found the solubility of alkyd resins in hydrocarbon solvents to be a function of the oil length of the resin, the solubility parameter, and the molar volume of the solvent.

L. J. Baranyai [1] presented a method for calculating the viscosity of alkyd resins in various solvents based on the viscosity and viscosity factor of the solvents. Calculated viscosities were in close agreement with actual viscosities.

L. Dintenfass [6] studied the viscosity behavior of many types of paint vehicles including alkyds. In an ideal solvent, total dispersion takes place giving Newtonian flow. With poorer solvents aggregation takes place giving a dilatant or even thixotropic system. This investigator also studied the molecular weights in relation to viscosity of a number of paint vehicles including alkyds.[7]

W. W. Reynolds [13] reported the effect of solvent properties on the viscosity of alkyd resin solutions. It was found that the viscosity of a long-oil alkyd solution was essentially independent of the solvent power of the solvent as judged by hydrocarbon compositions, Kauri Butanol, aniline cloud point, and solubility parameter. In sharp contrast, the viscosity of blends of hydrocarbon solvents with a short-oil resin was found to be strongly dependent upon the solvent power of the hydrocarbon composition.

Degree of Esterification

D. W. Berryman [2] did some work on the relation between degree of esterification and properties of alkyd resins. In general the air-drying and baking potential reaches a maximum as the polymer size of the alkyd approaches the gel point. It was also found that alkyds cooked at higher temperatures showed premature gloss drop on exposure.

Film Formation Properties and Deterioration

Several alkyds were included in an extensive study [8] that was made of film formation, film properties, and film deterioration by the Research Committee of the Federation of Paint & Varnish Production Clubs.

Adhesion

J. S. Long [10] reported on a method of predicting the adhesion of alkyds based on the number of molecules of phthalic anhydride per mole resin, the number of hydroxyl groups in the polyol, and the number of double bonds in each fatty acid segment.

Exposure to Ultraviolet Light

J. S. Long [10] also reported on the relationship between chemical composition and the absorption of ultraviolet light by alkyds. The higher the percentage of fatty acid or oil, the higher the ultraviolet absorption.

E. Oakley [11] studied the gloss retention of alkyds on outdoor exposure. It was found that the degree of gloss failure was related directly to the amount of solar energy falling on the panels.

Irradiation

F. L. Kech [9] reported that a typical automotive or appliance finish (pigmented melamine-modified nonoxidizing alkyd) when subjected to beta irradiation underwent many interesting physical changes. When compared to similar baked films, the irradiated films had greater hardness and specular gloss. In a few formulations, pigment color was altered by beta irradiation. Electron photomicrographs indicated that film degradation after 350 hours in an XW Weatherometer was less for an irradiated film than for a comparable baked film.

Thermal Stability

A. L. Smith, *et al.*[15] studied the thermal stability of several alkyds and silicone resins by infrared spectroscopy. It was found that the isophthalic and terephthalic alkyds were superior to orthophthalic alkyds. However, they did not approach the silicone resin in performance. By their method, useful life at 200°C was:

Orthophthalic alkyd	42 hr
Isophthalic alkyd	2600 hr
Terephthalic alkyd	4100 hr
Silicone	900,000 hr (extrapolated)

Conversely, a life of 1000 hours is expected at temperatures of:

Orthophthalic alkyd	153°C
Isophthalic alkyd	215°C
Terephthalic alkyd	223°C
Silicone	350°C

Pigmentation and Physical Strength

W. Bosch [3] reported on the influence of fineness of grind and aging of liquid paint upon stress-strain properties of alkyd paint films. Three pigments, chrome orange, zinc oxide and titanium dioxide, were evaluated at a 15 per cent pigment volume concentration. As expected, the elongation of the chrome orange and zinc oxide films decreased with age. With titanium dioxide the effect was slight. The older the liquid paint the greater was the elongation of the paint film. There was no correlation between fineness of grind and elongation.

References

1. Baranyai, L. J., *J. Oil & Colour Chemists' Assoc.*, **43**, No. 3, 214 (1960).
2. Berryman, D. W., *J. Oil & Colour Chemists' Assoc.*, **42**, No. 6, 393 (1959).
3. Bosch, W., and Wong, H. Y., *Offic. Dig.*, **27**, No. 371, 996 (1955).
4. Brett, R. A., *J. Oil & Colour Chemists' Assoc.*, **41**, No. 6, 428 (1958).
5. Bullett, T. R., and Rudran, A. T. S., *J. Oil & Colour Chemists' Assoc.*, **42**, No. 11, 778 (1959).
6. Dintenfass, L., *J. Oil & Colour Chemists' Assoc.*, **40**, No. 9, 761 (1957).
7. Dintenfass, L., *J. Oil & Colour Chemists' Assoc.*, **41**, No. 5, 333 (1958).
8. "Film Formation, Film Properties and Film Deterioration," New York, *Interscience Publishers, Inc.*, 1958. A study by the Research Committee of Federation of Paint & Varnish Production Clubs.

9. Kech, F. L., *Offic. Dig.*, **30**, No. 404, 989 (1958).
10. Long, J. S., *Offic. Dig.*, **32**, No. 420, 7 (1960).
11. Oakley, E., *J. Oil & Colour Chemists' Assoc.*, **43**, No. 3, 201 (1960).
12. Reynolds, W. W., *Offic. Dig.*, **29**, No. 393, 966 (1957).
13. Reynolds, W. W., Gebhart, H. J., Jr., *Offic. Dig.*, **29**, No. 394, 1174 (1957).
14. Seavell, A. J., *J. Oil & Colour Chemists' Assoc.*, **42**, No. 5, 319 (1959).
15. Smith, A. L., Brown, L. M., Tyler, L. J., Hunter, M. J., *Ind. Eng. Chem.*, **49**, No. 11, 1903 (1957).
16. Tawn, A. R. H., *J. Oil & Colour Chemists' Assoc.*, **39**, No. 4, 223 (1956).

8. UNMODIFIED ALKYDS

Unmodified or "straight" alkyds contain a dibasic acid, a polyol, and a fatty acid or oil. In some cases, especially in low-oil-content alkyds, a monofunctional material such as benzoic acid may be used to decrease functionality. Straight alkyds have good exterior durability with the short-oil types having better gloss retention and the longer oil types better long-term durability. Alkyds have good resistance to humidity or to intermittent water exposure such as rainfall, but are not recommended for water immersion applications. Alkyds give good protection against the corrosive effects of neutral salts but have poor alkali resistance. Dilute acids have less effect on the film than dilute alkalis. Alkyds are not resistant to concentrated acids, oxidizing acids, or strong organic acids.

Alkyds have fair resistance to petroleum solvents and oils. Films are softened by strong solvents such as alcohols and aromatic hydrocarbons and are removed by ketones, esters, and chlorinated solvents.

Alkyd films will stand continuous exposure at temperatures up to 250°F with little mechanical deterioration although light colors will darken. Alkyds give reasonable performance at temperatures up to 300°F but the film will become somewhat brittle.

Driers

The selection of the proper amount and type of drier is important to obtain the optimum performance of an alkyd. This is dependent upon the percentage of oil and the pigmentation, the type of application, and whether air-dry or bake. In certain formulations the drier is absorbed or deactivated on aging.[2]

Alcoholysis

An alkyd can be prepared by either a solvent- or fusion-type cook. The alkyd can be made directly from the fatty acid or indirectly from the drying oil by proceeding through an intermediate step known as alcoholysis. The oil and polyol are heated in the presence of a catalyst to form the monoglyceride. At this point the phthalic anhydride is added and the reaction completed.

This is an important step in the preparation of an alkyd as an improperly formed monoglyceride may cause haze, etc., and may even cause the alkyd to gel prematurely in cooking.

Various studies have been made to determine the optimum conditions for alcoholysis, selection of catalyst, and methods for determining the formation of a satisfactory monoglyceride.

Catalysts for Alcoholysis. Burrell[1] studied catalysts for the alcoholysis reaction and concluded that compounds of lead and lithium are the most efficient catalysts. Listed in order of effectiveness, they are:

Metal Catalyst	Efficiency
Pb	1
Li	1
Ca	3
Ba	4
Ce	5
Cd	6
Zn	7
St	8
Al, Bi, Co, Cr, Cu, Fe, Mg, Mn, Hg, Ni, Th	No activity

Other studies [6] showed that calcium hydroxide or naphthenate produce slightly better color than litharge but that the water resistance of the dried film is poorer. The time of alcoholysis varies with the type of oil used. The optimum temperature for alcoholysis was found to be about 450°F, using an amount of catalyst equivalent to 0.10-0.15 per cent metal content based on polyol.

Calcium or lead catalysts will react with phthalic anhydride causing a colloidal precipitate of metallic phthalates. The presence of any phthalic anhydride, such as sublimed phthalic anhydride on the lid of the kettle from a previous batch, will inactivate the catalyst and prevent the formation of a satisfactory monoglyceride. After a satisfactory monoglyceride is formed, the addition of phthalic anhydride in the normal procedure forms some colloidal precipitate of metallic phthalates which can be removed by filtration.

Test Methods for Alcoholysis. Tests are designed to give a rapid indication of the completion of the alcoholysis reaction. One such test is based on the solubility of the monoglyceride in anhydrous methanol. The oil is insoluble but as more monoglycerides are formed the mixture becomes soluble. This test is begun by putting a hot sample of the alcoholysis product into a graduate. An equal volume of anhydrous methanol is added and agitated. If the mixture is clear, an additional volume of methanol is added. Alcoholysis is considered to be complete if one volume of the alcoholysis product is soluble in two volumes of alcohol.

When pentaerythritol is used as the polyol it is sometimes difficult to measure alcoholysis. Occasionally a haze is noticed in the methanol dilution test although other tests show that alcoholysis is complete. Mraz [6] describes an alcoholysis test in which the extent of alcoholysis is followed by the amount of pentaerythritol precipitate as measured by light-scattering measurements.

F. Mort [5] describes a method of measuring the amount of monoglyceride formed in alcoholysis by conductivity measurements.

Since the properties of alkyds are dependent to a large extent upon the amount of oil they contain, they will be reviewed on this basis.

Short Oil Alkyds

These are of drying and nondrying types. The nondrying types are essentially plasticizers and are nonfilm-forming. They are used with other resins such as urea-formaldehyde, nitrocellulose, vinyls, etc. The drying types can be used alone or in combination with other materials.

Properties are as follows:

> Drying: Fast setting
> Fair air drying
> Good baking
> Fair flexibility
> Good adhesion
> Good color
> Good color retention
> Good gloss
> Require aromatic solvents such
> as toluene and xylene
> Usual application, spray or dip

Short-oil alkyds containing soya or dehydrated castor oil are used in conjunction with amino resin for appliance finishes. Short-oil alkyds containing nondrying oils, such as coconut, are used in conjunction with nitrocellulose for automotive lacquers. Linseed short-oil alkyds by themselves can be used as fast air-drying or baking finishes.

The following is a short-oil soya alkyd made by the solvent process. Soya oil is used and converted to the monoglyceride by the alcoholysis method. This alkyd is suitable for use as a baking vehicle either by itself or in combination with an amino resin.

	Lb	Moles	Water Loss	Base Yield
Soya oil	160	.183		
Glycerin	110	1.210		
Phthalic anhydride	180	1.210	22 lb	
	450			428
Litharge catalyst	4 oz			
Xylene	428			

Fatty acids	35%		Excess hydroxyl	37.5%
Phthalic anhydride	42%		Functionality	1.95

Heat soya oil, glycerin and litharge to 450°F. Hold for clear by methanol test. Cool to 280°F. Add phthalic anhydride and 4 per cent xylene (18 lb) and heat up to reflux temperature. Cook for approximately 6 hr until characteristics are obtained. Thin with equal parts by weight of xylene.

Weight per gallon	8.25 lb
Viscosity	Z_1
Color	6
Acid value	4.0
NVM	50%

Figure 8.1 shows progress of cooking of this alkyd.

This vehicle possesses excellent compatibility with pigments along with such grinding properties as good pigment wetting and mill stability. This type of vehicle can be used in:

Appliance finishes
    Cabinets
    Furniture
    Refrigerators
    Venetian blinds
    Toys
Maintenance enamels
Anti-rust primers
Nitrocellulose lacquer plasticizers

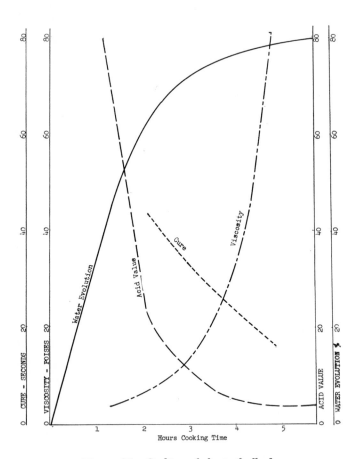

Figure 8.1. Cooking of short-oil alkyd.

Compatibility with:

Pigments	Excellent
Nitrocellulose	Excellent
Alkyds —short	Good
medium	Fair
long	Poor
Varnishes—short	Fair
medium	Poor
long	Poor
Oils	Poor
Bodied oils	Poor

Drying:

Air dry, set	15 min
Air dry, hard	4-5 hr
Bake	25-50 min @ 250-275°F
with 10-30% urea	5-45 min @ 300-325°F
with 10-30% melamine	15-45 min @ 250-275°F

Drier recommendations:

	Air Dry	Bake
Lead	None	None
Manganese	None	None
Cobalt	0.03-0.07%	0.01-0.02%
Calcium	0.2 -0.4 %	None
Zinc	None	0.1%

Formulations:

White Cabinet Enamel

Lb	Gal		
275	8.6	Anatase titanium dioxide	
160	20.0	35% Soya alkyd (50% NVM)	} Grind
15	2.0	Pine oil	
296	37.0	35% Soya alkyd (50% NVM)	
111	13.0	Melamine, 50% solution	
36	5.0	Xylene	} Add to
134	18.0	Naphtha	let down
7.7	1.0	Ethyl alcohol	
1034.7	104.6		

Viscosity 17″ No. 4 Ford Cup—20% reduction xylene
Spray   Reduce with xylene, 15-20%
Bake   15 min @ 300°F

Blue Toy Enamel

Lb	Gal		
40	3.2	Solfast blue	Grind, ball mill for 8-12 hr
10	0.3	Rutile titanium dioxide	
164	20.0	35% Soya alkyd (50% NVM)	
7	1.0	Pine oil	
502	61.0	35% Soya alkyd (50% NVM)	
9	1.0	6% Cobalt naphthenate	
58	8.0	Xylene	
4	0.5	8% Zinc naphthenate	
53	8.5	VM&P naphtha	
847	103.5		

Weight per gallon   8.20 lb
Bake   25 min @ 275°F

Medium Oil Alkyds

These are the most versatile of alkyds and have the following properties:

Good water impermeability
Fair baking   Fair color
Usual application, brush, spray or dip
Require aliphatic solvents such as mineral spirits and naphthas

Medium-oil alkyds are used for both air-drying and baking applications. The modifying oil is usually linseed or soya. Alkyds of this type are used for machinery enamels, drum enamels and other industrial applications.

The following is a medium-length tall oil fatty acids cook prepared by the fusion method, used for both air-drying and baking applications:

	Lb	Moles	Loss	Yield
Tall oil fatty acids	200	.69		
Pentaerythritol	100	2.92		
Phthalic anhydride	120	1.61	40.0	
	420			380
Mineral spirits	380			

Fatty acid	50%	Excess hydroxyl	27%
Phthalic anhydride	33%	Functionality	2.08

Heat tall oil fatty acids, pentaerythritol and phthalic anhydride to a temperature of 550°F in a kettle fitted with a steam condenser. After 1 hr of heating, sparge with inert gas until acid value of 10 is reached. Total time will be about 6 hr. Reduce with equal parts of mineral spirits.

Weight per gallon	7.60 lb
Color	8
Acid value/solids	10
Viscosity	Y
NVM	50%

This vehicle can be used in:

Industrial finishes
   Farm implement enamels
   Railroad car finishes
   Hardware enamels
   Metal furniture enamels
   Metal primers
Automotive refinishing enamels
Specification finishes
Traffic paints
Roller coat finishes

This vehicle has good pigment compatibility: the most difficult pigments being dispersable with ease. With reactive pigments such as zinc oxide it is recommended that the amount of zinc oxide used does not exceed 25 to 30 lb per 100 gal of finished enamel.

Compatibility with:

Pigments	Good
Nitrocellulose	None
Alkyds —short	Fair
medium	Good
long	Good
Varnishes—short	Fair
medium	Good
long	Good
Oils	Good
Bodied oils	Fair

Drying:

Air dry, set	30 min
Air dry, hard	6-8 hr
Bake	1 hr @ 275-300°F

Drier recommendations:

	Air Dry	Bake
Lead	0.1 -0.3%	None
Manganese	0.01-0.03%	None
Cobalt	0.02-0.03%	0.01-0.02%
Calcium (to replace lead)	0.2 -0.4%	None
Zinc	None	0.11-0.2%

Formulations:

Green Maintenance Enamel

Lb	Gal		
35	1.2	Chrome green	Grind.
150	5.5	Titanium calcium	Roller
4	0.5	Soya lecithin	mill to
150	20.0	50% Tall oil alkyd (50% NVM)	6H grind
428	54.0	50% Tall oil alkyd (50% NVM)	
10	1.0	28% Lead naphthenate	
6	0.6	6% Cobalt naphthenate	
130	20.0	Mineral spirits	
913	102.8		

Weight per gallon	8.75 lb
Viscosity	72-74 K.U.

Railroad Car Primer

Lb	Gal		
266	7.4	Iron oxide	Grind.
188	6.4	Zinc chromate	Ball
77	3.2	Magnesium silicate	mill
5	0.6	Calcium stearate	10-12
209	27.5	50% Tall oil alkyd (50% NVM)	hr
9	0.9	24% Lead naphthenate	
1	0.1	Anti-skinning agent	
66	9.2	Xylene	
289	38.0	50% Tall oil alkyd (50% NVM)	
5	0.6	6% Manganese naphthenate	
5	0.6	6% Cobalt	
61	8.5	Xylene	
1181	103.0		

Weight per gallon	11.55 lb
Viscosity	70 K.U.

Long-Oil Alkyds

Properties of long-oil alkyds are:

Flexibility
Good durability
Application, brush
Require aliphatic solvents such as mineral spirits
Slow drying

Long-oil alkyds are used for interior and exterior finishes in the architectural, maintenance and marine fields. Following is a long-oil linseed glyceryl phthalate alkyd made by the fusion process. The alcoholysis step is used with the linseed oil. This alkyd can be used in architectural type finishes and is suitable for exterior use.

	Lb	Moles	Loss	Base Yield
Linseed oil	360	1.22		
Glycerin	80	2.57		
Phthalic anhydride	160	2.17		
	600		−30	570
Litharge	4 oz.			
Mineral spirits				244
				814

Heat linseed oil and glycerin to 500°F, add litharge and hold for clear with methanol. Add phthalic anhydride. Cook until acid value of 10 is reached. Reduce to 70 per cent solids with mineral spirits.

Oil	63%
Weight per gallon	8.10 lb
Color	10
Acid value	7
Viscosity	Z
NVM	70%

This type of vehicle produces paints having excellent brushing and flow properties.

Compatibility with:

Pigments	Excellent
Nitrocellulose	None
Alkyds —short	Fair
medium	Good
long	Excellent
Varnishes—short	Fair
medium	Good
long	Excellent
Oils	Excellent
Bodied oil	Excellent

Drying and drier recommendations:

Air dry, set	2½ hr
Air dry, hard	6-8 hr

	Air Dry
Lead	0.3 -0.6%
Manganese	None
Cobalt	0.03-0.06%
Calcium (to replace lead)	0.3 -0.6%
Zinc	None

This vehicle can be used in the following applications (do not use in whites):

Industrial

Maintenance finishes
Marine finishes
Awning paints
Silk screen finishes
Highway maintenance

Shelf goods

Trim and trellis paints
Household enamels
Lawn furniture

Formulations:

Hull Paint

Lb	Gal		
300	7.6	Iron oxide	
170	7.4	Micronized talc	
32	0.7	Zinc oxide	Grind
278	35.0	63% Linseed alkyd (70% NVM)	
39	6.0	Mineral spirits	
215	27.0	63% Linseed alkyd (70% NVM)	
117	15.0	Mineral spirits	
30	4.0	4% Calcium naphthenate	
3	0.3	6% Cobalt naphthenate	
1184	103.0		

Weight per gallon   11.40 lb
For brushing, reduce 15% with mineral spirits

Red Exterior Enamel

Lb	Gal		
100	8.6	Toluidine red	
46	2.0	Micronized talc	
2	0.2	Soya lecithin	Grind
4	0.4	Calcium stearate	
240	30.0	63% Linseed alkyd (70% NVM)	
280	35.0	63% Linseed alkyd (70% NVM)	
78	10.0	"D"-bodied linseed oil	
98	15.0	Mineral spirits	
10	1.0	24% Lead naphthenate	
5	0.6	6% Cobalt naphthenate	
2	0.2	Anti-skinning agent	
865	103.0		

Weight per gallon   8.42 lb
Brushing   Reduce 5% with mineral spirits
Spraying   Reduce 20% with VM&P naphtha

Use of Maleic Anhydride or Fumaric Acid to Speed Cooking

The replacement of a small amount of phthalic anhydride with maleic anhydride or fumaric acid in an alkyd may be used to decrease the cooking time. These unsaturated acids form addition products with the double bonds of the drying oil. This reaction increases the functionality of the system and causes more rapid bodying. Since cooking time is shortened, the final color is sometimes lighter.

Below are shown two 62 per cent soya PE alkyd resins cooked by the fusion process. In the second alkyd, 2 per cent of the phthalic anhydride is replaced with fumaric acid. Esterification was carried out at a temperature of 480°F.

	Control Alkyd * (all phthalic)			Fumaric Alkyd * 2% fumaric 98% phthalic		
Hr @ 480°F	Acid No.	Visc.	Color	Acid No.	Visc.	Color
1	25	F	6+	26	I	5
2	18	H	6+	20	K	5
3	15	J	6+	17	M	5
4	12	L	6+	15	O	5
5	10	O	6+	12	R	5
6	9	P	6+	10	T	6+
6½	8	R	7	9	W	6+

Drying Data: 0.5% lead and 0.005% cobalt

Drying:	*Control*	*Fumaric*
Set to touch	150 min	140 min
Dry hard	6 hr	5½ hr

* *Courtesy Monsanto Chemical Co.*

Use of Monofunctional Reactants

Monofunctional aromatic acids are sometimes incorporated into an alkyd as a "molecular chain stopper." The alkyd can be cooked to a lower acid value without the danger of gelation. R. L. Heinrich, *et al.*[3] studied the effectiveness of substituted monocarboxylic aromatic acids as alkyd resin modifiers. The aromatic acids usually used are benzoic and paratertiary butyl benzoic.

Shown below is a 33 per cent linseed glycerin alkyd made by alcoholysis,* replacing part of the phthalic with Benthal † (95 per cent benzoic acid).

* Courtesy Monsanto Chemical Co.
† Trade name, Monsanto Chemical Co.

Benthal Replacement of * Phthalic, Anhydride (%)	Time to Gel at 430°F (Min)	Acid Value (Solids)
0	49	60
8	64	45
10	75	30
15	120	15

Shown below are three 33 per cent soya oil alkyds which have been formulated using Benthal (95 per cent benzoic acid) and reducing functionality by using excess glycerin and glycol.

33% Soya Oil Alkyds *

Ingredients	Using Benthal	Using Excess Glycerin	Using Ethylene Glycol
Step 1:			
Alkali-refined soya oil	94.5	94.5	94.5
Calcium hydroxide	0.053	0.053	0.053
Glycerin, 98%	23.5	23.5	23.5
Step 2:			
Glycerin, 98%	39.0	47.0	39.0
Phthalic anhydride	113.0	120.0	120.0
Benthal	16.7	—	—
Ethylene glycol	—	—	9.0
Glycerin:Phthalic ratio	2.4:3	2.85:3	2.4:3

* Courtesy Monsanto Chemical Co.

All three formulations were processed in the same manner, as follows:

The ingredients for Step 1 were cooked at 450°F for one-half hour with rapid agitation and CO_2 blanket. Alcoholysis was checked by mixing one part of the cooked oil with four parts of anhydrous methanol and heating to the methanol boiling point. The mixture was clear indicating proper alcoholysis.

At the completion of Step 1, the ingredients for Step 2 were added and the batch brought from 290 to 440°F over a 1-hour heating period. Processing continued at 440°F until the final acid number and viscosity values were reached. Tabulated below are properties of the three resins.*

	Benthal Modification	Excess Glycerin Modification	Ethylene Glycol Modification
Alkyd Resin Properties			
Acid number (solids)	13.6	12.2	14.0
Viscosity (50% Solids in xylene)	Y	Y	X-Y
Color (Gardner)	4-5	4-5	5
Time of cook @ 440°F	135 min	109 min	120 min
Excess glycerin	20%	42.5%	20%
% Solids in xylene to viscosity of F	36	40	43
Clear Film Properties:			
Air dry (0.5 lead, 0.05 cobalt)			
Set	15 min	15 min	15 min
Dry hard	205 min	225 min	215 min
Sward hardness (3 days)	38	34	32
Baked ½ hr @ 250°F			
Sward hardness	33	29 (Sl. wrinkle)	28 (Sl. wrinkle)
Alkali resistance			
Air dry 3 days, 2% NaOH	OK 5 min	Gone 4 min	Gone, 3 min
Baked 1 hr 250°F, 2% NaOH	OK 1 hr	Sl. spot 1 hr	Bad spot 1 hr
Water resistance (cold)			
Air dry 3 days	OK 2 hr	Sl. whitening	Very sl. whitening

* Courtesy Monsanto Chemical Co.

	Benthal Modification	Excess Glycerin Modification	Ethylene Glycol Modification
Durability of two clear coats on wood after 2 years exposure	OK	Film gone	Test incomplete, not concurrent with other two
Gloss (TiO_2 rutile: alkyd solids 50:50 ball milled 24 hr and baked on steel)	Best gloss	Worst gloss	Good gloss

Polymerized Fatty Acids

Polymerized fatty acids are sometimes used in an alkyd as a viscosity promoter. In some cases it also produces other desirable advantages such as through-drying, decreased wrinkling, and greater flexibility.

Dimer acids can be produced from linoleic acid by polymerizing under heat and pressure in the presence of water. The water prevents the degradation usually associated with thermal polymerization. The product consists essentially of dimer with small amounts of monomer and trimer. The exact structure of the dimer acid is not known and may range from a single carbon-to-carbon bond to a complex cyclic structure.

The structure will be shown singly as:

$$RCH\text{-}R\text{-}COOH$$
$$R_2CH \ R_3 \ COOH$$

Properties of a typical commercial dimer acid.[*]

Specifications:

Acid value	186-194	Color, Gardner	11 max
Saponification value	191-199	Neutralization equiv.	289-301
Unsaponifiable	2% max	Ash content	0.1% max

[*] Courtesy Emery Industries, Inc., Empol 1022.

Characteristics:

Dimer content	75%
Trimer content	22%
Monomer content	3%
Specific gravity at 15.5°C/15.5°C	0.95
Flash point, °F	530
Fire point, °F	600
Viscosity @ 25°C (Gardner-Holdt)	Z_4

The viscosity-promoting effects of polymerized fatty acids on an alkyd cook are shown below:

Medium-Oil Soya Alkyd *

(60% nonvolatile in xylene)

	None	10% phthalic replaced	20% phthalic replaced
Soya fatty acids	47.5	43.2	39.5
Glycerin	13.4	12.2	11.2
Pentaerythritol	7.7	7.0	6.4
Phthalic anhydride	31.4	25.8	20.9
Empol 1022	—	11.8	22.0
Acid number	1.0	1.6	0.8
Viscosity	U	Z_2	Gel
Processing time	5½ hr	4 hr	3 hr

Processed at 475°F in an inert atmosphere. All formulations are parts by weight.

* Courtesy Emery Industries, Inc.

References

1. Burrell, H., *Oil & Soap,* **21,** 206 (1944).
2. Dintenfass, L., *J. Oil & Colour Chemists' Assoc.,* **43,** 709-19 (1960).
3. Heinrich, R. L., *et al.,* Papers Presented at the Boston Meeting, American Chemical Society, Division of Paint, Plastics, and Printing Ink Chemistry, **19,** No. 1, 241-48 (1959).
4. "The Chemistry and Processing of Alkyd Resins," Chapter IV, Monsanto Chemical Co., 1952.
5. Mort, F., *J. Oil & Colour Chemists' Assoc.,* **39,** 253-61 (1956).
6. Mraz, R. G., Silver, R. P., and Coden, C. O., *Offic. Dig.,* **29,** 256-71 (1957).

9. MODIFIED ALKYDS

Alkyds can be modified with numerous other resins to impart some of the desirable characteristics of these resins. In many cases, since the modifying resin is more soluble in aliphatic solvents than the glyceryl phthalate resin, it is possible to formulate short-oil rapid-drying vehicles which are soluble in aliphatic solvents. Theoretically, it is possible to modify an alkyd with any resinous material which contains reactive acid or alcohol groups. However, there are practical limitations such as the solubility of the modifying resin and whether it will stand the cooking temperatures involved in alkyd production. These modifying resins or materials when cooked in an alkyd are reacted by esterification reactions and are thereby an integral part of the alkyd resin. Modification of alkyd with rosin, rosin maleic resins, congo resin, and rosin alcohol imparts fast-drying properties to the alkyd. Phenolic resin modification imparts fast drying as well as improved alkali resistance. Epoxy resins, which can only be used in small amounts because of their high functionality, can be used to produce alkyds of extremely high viscosity. Silicone resin will improve the heat resistance of the alkyd. To produce thixotropic alkyds for use in "gelled paint," polyamides are used to modify the alkyd. Isocyanates are sometimes incorporated in an alkyd to reduce terminal hydroxy groups and thereby improve the over-all properties. The modifications described in this chapter are carried out by reacting or "tying up" with the alkyd resin, usually in the cooking operation.

Rosin Modification

Rosin is a modifier which will lower the cost of an alkyd and impart fast-drying properties. It does, however, produce a darker color and give decreased durability.

Rosin is a natural product and is, therefore, not a pure chemical compound. It consists of about 90 per cent resin acids and 10 per cent neutral material. The principal acid is abietic acid which may be isomerized to levopimaric acid by heat.

Since rosin is an acidic material it will react with polyol to form resinous materials; for example, rosin and glycerin form ester gum. Therefore, if rosin is included in an alkyd formulation, a rosin ester will be formed along with the phthalate ester and these will be tied together along with the fatty acid or oil.

Properties of a 55 per cent linseed glycerol PE alkyd are shown below:

	Rosin-Modified	Unmodified
Oil	55% Linseed	55% Linseed
Resin	32% Phthalic PE	45% Phthalic PE
	13% Rosin PE	
NVM	50	50
Solvent	Mineral spirits	Mineral spirits
Viscosity	F	Y
Color	9	8
Drying time (tack-free)	6 hr	8 hr
Durability	Good	Excellent

Note that modification with rosin reduces viscosity because of the reduced functionality and improved solubility in mineral spirits of the rosin as compared to phthalic anhydride. The rosin-modified alkyd is faster drying and has better through-drying because of faster solvent release. Since commercial tall oils contain up to 45 per cent rosin it is possible to produce rosin-modified alkyds economically by the use of the proper tall oil.

A typical short oil rosin-modified alkyd is as follows:

Oil	42%
Rosin	28%
NVM	50%
Solvent	Mineral spirits
Viscosity	X-Z_2
Color	11
Acid value	15
Weight/gal	7.62 lb

This vehicle can be used for spray, brush, or dip application. High-quality finishes can be prepared with the use of this alkyd in:

Farm implement finishes	Hardware enamels
Freight car finishes	Furniture clears
Drum enamels	Metal primers
Toy enamels	Automotive refinishing enamels
	Automotive chassis enamels

Compatibility with:

Pigments	Good
Nitrocellulose	Fair
Alkyds —short	Fair
medium	Good
long	Good
Varnishes—short	Fair
medium	Good
long	Good
Oils	Good
Bodied oils	Fair

Drying and drier recommendations:

Air dry, set	30-60 min
Air dry, hard	6-8 hr
Bake	200-300°F for 45 min to 2 hr

	Air Dry	Bake
Lead	0.3 -0.5%	0.2%
Manganese	0.01-0.03%	0.02%
Cobalt	0.01-0.03%	0.02%
Zinc	None	0.1%

Paint formulations:

Blue Gray Lusterless Enamel

Lb	Gal		
106.0	3.0	Titanium dioxide, rutile	
2.0	.13	Lampblack	Ball mill
270.0	11.50	Talc	10-12 hr
4.0	.40	Lecithin	
244.0	32.0	Short-oil rosin-modified alkyd	
15.0	.5	24% Lead naphthenate	
75.0	13.0	VM&P naphtha	
111.0	14.5	Short-oil rosin-modified alkyd	
14.0	0.7	6% Manganese naphthenate	
155.0	27.0	VM&P naphtha	
7.0	0.8	6% Cobalt naphthenate	
1.0	0.1	Anti-skinning agent	
1004.0	103.63		

Weight per gallon   9.70 lb
Application   Spray, reduce 25% with VM&P naphtha

Rosin Maleic Modifications

When rosin is reacted with maleic anhydride it undergoes the Diels-Alder reaction to produce a trifunctional acid which can be reacted with polyols to give resins with higher melting points.

It is possible to produce maleate-modified alkyds by adding the previously prepared resin in the alkyd cook or to

Levopimaric Acid   Maleic Anhydride   Adduct

prepare *in situ* by adding the maleic anhydride and rosin to the cook. However, when it is done in this manner it is also possible that the maleic anhydride will react with certain conjugated drying oils. A maleic-modified alkyd would be as follows:

Oil	35% Soya
Resin	22% Maleic rosin
	43% Glyceryl phthalate
NVM	50%
Solvent	70% Xylene
	30% VM&P naphtha
Color	9
Viscosity	V
Drying time (tack-free)	4 hr

Typical uses for a vehicle of this type would be:

Metal primers
Automotive primers
Drum enamels
Machinery enamels
Hardware enamels
Metal decorating enamels
Furniture clears

Compatibility with:

Pigments	Good
Nitrocellulose	Good
Alkyds —short	Good
medium	Good
long	Poor
Varnishes—short	Good
medium	Good
long	Poor
Oils	Poor
Bodied oils	Poor

Drying and drier recommendations:

Air dry, set	15 min
Air dry, hard	5-6 hr
Bake	225-275°F for 20-40 min

	Air Dry	Bake
Lead	0.3 -0.5%	0.2%
Manganese	0.01-0.03%	None
Cobalt	0.02-0.05%	0.01%
Calcium (to replace lead)	0.3 -0.5%	0.02%

Paint formulations:

Gray Baking Primer

Lb	Gal		
285	8.9	Anatase titanium dioxide	
190	5.4	Titanium barium	
135	6.1	Whiting	
4	0.4	Aluminum stearate	Ball mill
4	0.4	Lampblack	24 hr
301	38.0	Short-oil maleic-rosin alkyd	
115	16.0	Xylene	
1	0.1	Anti-skinning agent	
143	18.0	Short-oil maleic-rosin alkyd	
5	0.6	6% Manganese naphthenate	
2.5	0.3	6% Cobalt naphthenate	
63	9.0	Xylene	
1248.5	103.2		

Weight per gallon	12.10 lb
Force dry	30 min @ 120°F

Gray Drum Enamel

Lb	Gal		
400	10.8	Lithopone	
1	0.1	Lampblack	
198	25.0	Short-oil maleic-rosin alkyd	
13	1.3	24% Lead naphthenate	Grind 16 hr
8	1.0	6% Manganese naphthenate	ball mill
2.5	0.3	6% Cobalt naphthenate	
65	8.0	Xylene	
2	0.15	Anti-skinning agent	
254	32.0	Short-oil maleic-rosin alkyd	
108	15.0	Xylene	
65	10.0	Mineral spirits	
1116.5	103.6		

Weight per gallon	10.90 lb
Force dry	20 min @ 180°F

Rosin Alcohol Modified Alkyds

Rosin can be hydrogenated and the acid group converted to an alcohol group. Such a material has the trade name Abitol.* Commercially, this is a mixture of 45 per cent tetrahydroabietyl alcohol, 40 per cent dihydroabietyl alcohol (one double bond) and 15 per cent dehydroabietyl alcohol (three double bonds).

Figure 9.1. Drum enamel finishing line. Many drum enamels are based on resin-modified alkyd formulas. (*Courtesy Sherwin-Williams Co.*)

The use of a monofunctional alcohol reduces the gelling tendency of the formulation. It is possible, therefore, to cook to a lower acid value and higher molecular weight without gelling. A specific example of a hydrogenated rosin alcohol-modified alkyd † is as follows:

* Hercules Powder Co.
† Courtesy Hercules Powder Co.

	Weight (in grams)	Equivalent
"Q" Soya oil	146.5	1.00 fatty acids
Alkali-refined soya oil	146.5	1.00 glycerin
Pentaerythritol	92.0	2.60
Phthalic anhydride	148.0	2.00
Hydrogenated rosin alcohol	56.0	0.16
Litharge	0.08	

$$\text{Excess hydroxyl} = \frac{(3.76 - 3.00) \times 100}{3} = 25.3\% \text{ excess}$$

$$\text{Functionality} = \frac{6.121}{2.92} = 2.09$$

The cooking schedule on this alkyd is as follows: *

Time	Temp. °C	Solid Acid No.	Visc. @ 30% Solids in Soltrol 130 †	Color	
0	Heat on				Charge soya oil, blanket with carbon dioxide 0.04 CFM/gal.
1:30	240				Add litharge and pentaerythritol.
2:00	240				Hold for monoglyceride, add Abitol and phthalic anhydride.
2:10	201				Carbon dioxide through batch.
2:45	230				
3:45	"	21.0	A	—	
4:45	"	13.5	A	—	
6:15	"	9.3	B	—	
6:45	"	5.8	D	—	
7:15	"	4.2	E-F	—	
7:45	"	3.7	G	—	
8:15	"	—	J	—	
8:45	"	—	O-P	—	
9:05	"	—	S	5-6	
9:25					Drop resin, reduce to 30% solids in Soltrol 130.

Characteristics: Acid value

	(NVM)	3.3
	Viscosity	U-V
	Color	5-6

* Courtesy Hercules Powder Co.
† Trade-mark, Phillips Petroleum Co. (Odorless Mineral Spirits)

A flat-wall finish using this alkyd * follows. Pigment volume concentration is 63 per cent.

Lb	Gal		
93.10	2.66	Ti-Pure R110 [1]	
324.10	11.93	Titanox RCHT [2]	
75.90	3.20	Asbestine 3X [3]	
75.90	3.36	Snoflake whiting [4]	
48.30	2.59	Celite 281 [5]	Grind
3.45	0.41	Aluminum distearate	
5.50	0.41	Nuact paste [6]	
410.30	59.52	Alkyd	
1.40	0.17	Bartyl A [7]	
2.11	0.17	6% Cobalt naphthenate	
101.40	16.13	Soltrol 130 [8]	
1141.46	100.55		

Total solids	65.5%
Weight per gallon	11.4 lb
Pigment by weight	54.3%

[1] Trade-mark, E. I. duPont de Nemours & Co., Inc.

[2] Trade-mark, Titanium Pigments Corp.

[3] International Pulp Co.

[4] Thompson, Weinman & Co.

[5] Trade-mark, Elliot Paint & Varnish Co.

[6] Trade-mark, Nuodex Products Co.

[7] Sinder Corp.

[8] Trade-mark, Phillips Petroleum Co.

Flat alkyd paints [2,3,4] produce a finish coat with better color and sheen uniformity than other type paints. Flat alkyd paints usually flow out better than latex paints and a thicker film can be applied. Because hydrocarbon thinners, which evaporate much more slowly than water, are used it is possible to obtain a much longer wet edge with flat alkyd vehicles. The alkyd molecule for this type of application is quite large as viscosities are in the range of T to Z_2 (Gardner-Holdt) at 30 per cent nonvolatile. In a normal applica-

* Courtesy Hercules Powder Co.

tion the alkyd flat is applied over a latex primer-sealer. This is rapid drying so it is possible to apply the two coats without moving staging.

Phenolic Modified Alkyd Resins

The addition of a phenolic resin improves drying as well as the water and alkali resistance. However, since the resultant varnish is darker in color their use is limited to certain applications. Phenolic resins, themselves, can be modified with rosin and other resins so that both modified phenolics and 100 per cent pure oil-soluble phenolic resins are used in combination with alkyds. In order to have an oil-soluble resin, substituted phenols are used. A typical reaction showing *p-tert* amylphenol and formaldehyde is:

Note that the phenolic resin has both alcoholic and phenolic hydroxyl groups. The alcoholic hydroxyl groups will react with organic acids while the phenolic hydroxide will react with the unsaturated double bonds in fatty acids and oils.

The incorporation of a phenolic resin in a tung oil alkyd permits cooking to a lower acid value with less danger of gelling. Alkyds of this type have fast-drying characteristics, good exterior durability, toughness and flexibility along with good mar and scratch resistance. Typical characteristics of an alkyd of this type would be:

Oil	35% Soya
	16% Tung
Phenolic	3%

NVM	50%
Solvent	70% Xylene
	30% VM&P naphtha
Viscosity	T-V
Color	10
Acid value	10

This is a fast drying medium-length pure phenolic-modified alkyd. Finishes made with an alkyd of this type have excellent durability, toughness, and flexibility along with mar and scratch resistance. Finishes of this type may be air-dried, force-dried or baked.

A medium oil length pure phenolic alkyd of this type can be used in the following applications:

> Automotive enamels
> Farm implement enamels
> Truck finishes
> Railroad passenger car finishes
> Tractor finishes

Compatibility with:

Pigments	Fair
Nitrocellulose	Fair
Alkyds —short	Fair
medium	Good
long	Fair
Varnishes—short	Fair
medium	Good
long	Fair
Oils	Fair
Bodied oils	Fair

Drying and drier recommendations:

Air dry, set	15 min
Air dry, hard	3-4 hr
Bake	220° to 280°F for 30 to 60 min

	Air Dry	Bake
Lead	0.3 -0.5%	0.15%
Manganese	0.07-0.13%	0.03%
Cobalt	0.02-0.05%	0.02%
Zinc	None	0.2%
Calcium	0.1 -0.3%	None

Paint formulations:

Orange Truck Enamel

Lb	Gal		
120.0	2.1	Chrome orange	⎫
118.0	15.0	Medium-oil-length phenolic- modified alkyd	⎬ Roller mill,
32.0	5.0	Mineral spirits	6-7H
21.6	3.0	High solvency naphtha	grind
9.6	1.0	24% Lead naphthenate	
1.0	0.15	Anti-skinning agent	⎭
482.0	61.5	Medium-oil-length phenolic- modified alkyd	
88.0	13.5	Mineral spirits	
4.0	0.5	6% Cobalt naphthenate	
2.4	0.3	6% Manganese naphthenate	
7.8	1.0	4% Calcium naphthenate	
886.4	103.05		

Weight per gallon 8.60 lb
Viscosity, No. 4 Ford Cup 60-75 sec
Spray Reduce with xylene 20-30%
Dry—slight tack ½ hr
    dry 4-6 hr

Gold Implement Finish

Lb	Gal		
274.0	5.45	Chrome yellow	⎫
18.0	.44	Light red iron oxide	⎬ Roller mill,
3.0	.34	Soya lecithin	6-7H
157.0	20.00	Medium-oil-length phenolic- modified alkyd	grind
360.0	46.0	Medium-oil-length phenolic- modified alkyd	
10.0	1.5	15% Guaiacol	
6.0	0.85	24% Lead naphthenate	
5.0	0.65	6% Manganese naphthenate	
5.0	0.65	6% Cobalt naphthenate	
112.0	18.00	VM&P naphtha	
71.0	9.85	Xylene	
1021.0	103.7		

Weight per gallon 9.81 lb
Viscosity, No. 4 Ford Cup 65-75 sec

One interesting application of phenolic-modified alkyds is in wrinkle finishes. An alkyd containing a conjugated oil, such as tung or oiticica, will wrinkle under certain conditions. This property is used to advantage in producing this type of novelty finish. Wrinkle-finish vehicles usually contain between 40 and 50 per cent oil. The greater the amount of oil the larger is the wrinkling pattern produced.

A typical alkyd used for wrinkle finishes would be as follows:

Oil	51% Tung
Modified phenolic	28%
NVM	50%
Solvent	70% Xylene
	30% VM&P naphtha
Viscosity	G-I
Color	12
Acid value	50

A typical wrinkle-finish formulation follows:

Black Wrinkle Finish

Lb	Gal		
7.0	0.5	Lampblack	
5.0	0.3	Carbon black	
35.0	1.9	Magnesium carbonate	
2.0	0.2	Lecithin	Roller mill,
166.0	21.0	Medium-oil-length phenolic-modified alkyd	4H grind
34.0	4.7	Xylene	
2.0	0.2	Guaiacol solution	
400.0	51.5	Medium-oil-length phenolic-modified alkyd	
16.0	1.8	6% Cobalt naphthenate	
101.0	16.3	VM&P naphtha	
36.0	5.0	Toluene	
804.0	103.4		

Weight per gallon	7.7 lb
Viscosity No. 4 Ford Cup	65-75 sec
Bake	225°-250°F for 30 min
Spray application	

Figure 9.2 shows a typical wrinkle finish. Wrinkle finishes are used because they produce a rich, tough, long-lasting textured finish. They cover surface blemishes, weld marks and minor imperfections in a one-coat application.

Figure 9.2. Fine, medium and coarse wrinkle finishes. (*Courtesy Sherwin-Williams Co.*)

Epoxy Alkyd Resins

Epoxy resins can be used to a limited extent to modify alkyd resins for improved chemical resistance.[6] Epoxy resins contain an epoxy or alcohol group which can be esterified. However, because of the high functionality of the epoxy resin, excessive viscosities are obtained which limit usability.

Shown below is a formulation for an epoxy-modified alkyd resin. This formulation was developed by the Shell Chemical Co. using Epon 1001.* Epon 1001 has an average of two hydroxy groups (OH) and two epoxy groups $(\overset{O}{\overset{/\backslash}{C-C}})$ per molecule. Each epoxy group will react with two moles of a monobasic acid, therefore we may think of the hydroxy function of Epon 1001 as being six in esterification reactions.

	Functionality	Monobasic Functionality
Epon 1001	2OH	2
	$2\,\overset{O}{\overset{/\backslash}{C-C}}$	$\dfrac{4}{6}$

If an alkyd is cooked with Epon 1001 resin directly, it will gel at a high acid number due to the high functionality of the epoxy resin. To overcome this, the epoxy resin is first cooked with a fatty acid.

	Mole	Functionality
Epon 1001	1	6
Fatty acid	3	$\dfrac{-3}{3}$

Therefore the functionality of the partially reacted epoxy resin is reduced to three, which is in the range of that of polyols usually used. This partially reacted epoxy resin is then used in an alkyd cook.

	Moles	Moles	F	Total F
Epon 1001 — 1 ⎫ Fatty acid — 3 ⎬ Partially reacted epoxy ester	¼	3	¾
Glycerin	¾	3	2¼
Phthalic anhydride	1	2	2
Fatty acid	$\dfrac{1}{3}$	1	$\dfrac{1}{6}$

$$\text{Functionality} = \frac{6}{3} = 2$$

* Registered Trade-mark, Shell Chemical Co.

Shown below is a baking-type epoxy-modified alkyd formula for an automotive primer: *

% Weight		Material
15.0		Phthalic anhydride
38.9		Tall oil (Acintal D) *
36.3 ⎱	49.5 Epon 1001	Partially reacted epoxy fatty
⎰	50.5 Tall oil	acid ester
9.8		Glycerin, 20% excess
100.0		

* Trade-mark Arizona Chemical Co.

Procedure for cooking is to charge epoxy resin and fatty acids into kettle, bring to 415°F and hold for acid value. Add glycerin and increase temperature to 450°F. Add phthalic anhydride one-half hour after glycerin addition, raise temperature again to 450°F and hold for acid value and viscosity.

Polyamide Alkyds

The incorporation of polyamide resins under certain conditions produces paint vehicles with "thixotropic" properties.[5] Thixotropy, or false body, is a phenomenon whereby the viscosity of a material is reduced with the increase of the shearing force. This is best illustrated by use of a rotational viscometer to plot torque against rate of shear (rotational speed). In Newtonian liquids the viscosity is independent of the rate of shear at a given temperature. Newtonian liquids, when plotted by this system, give a straight line through the origin. In dilatant fluids the viscosity increases with shear, giving a curve concave with respect to the torque axis. Pseudoplastic and thixotropic liquids both show viscosity decreasing with increasing shear and thus give curves convex with respect to the torque axis.

° Courtesy Shell Chemical Co.

In pseudoplastic liquids the down curve is identical with the up curve, while a thixotropic liquid gives a different curve since the viscosity does not return immediately to its previous value at any particular rate of shear (see Figure 9.3).

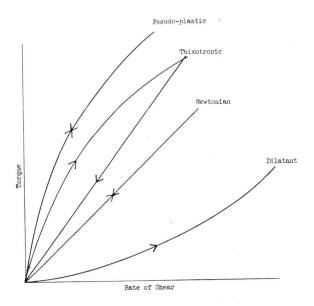

Figure 9.3. Stress-strain curves for various rheological types.

The particular advantage of thixotropic vehicles is that dripless and nonsagging paints can be produced. Pigment settling is eliminated in gel paints, they are nondripping in brush transfer, and the paint flows satisfactorily when a shear is applied in brushing. Flow-out is satisfactory so that brush marks disappear and the paint returns to its original false body on the surface to which it is applied in a few seconds; thus no sagging should occur. It has been found that the particular reaction of a polyamide resin with an oil

or an alkyd will produce a thixotropic vehicle. The polyamide is used in percentages up to 10 per cent of the alkyd
and is reacted at normal alkyd processing temperatures
(390-570°F).

The polyamide is first dispersed in the alkyd as droplets
and then slowly dissolves. At this point the alkyd shows
thixotropic gel-like properties when cooled. If heating is
continued, all gel structure will disappear and a nearly
Newtonian liquid will result.

It is believed that an amide and ester interchange reaction takes place between the alkyd and amide chains.

$$RCOOH + R'CONHR'' \longrightarrow R'COOH + RCONHR''$$
$$ROH \quad + R'CONHR'' \longrightarrow R'COOR + NH_2R''$$
$$R''NH_2 \quad + RCOOH \quad \longrightarrow RCONHR''$$

In the foregoing reaction R, R' and R'' are alkyd or polyamide molecular residues. The typical polyamide used has
an acid value and an amine value of about 4 (expressed as
mg KOH/g or equivalent), while the alkyd will have an
acid value around 10 and a hydroxyl value of 30 so that
there are sufficient end groups for the reaction.

The thixotropic behavior of these resins has been ascribed
to hydrogen bonding of the nitrogen atoms in the polyamide
chains. These hydrogen bonds lead to a temporary cross-
linked structure which disappears when the bonds are
broken by agitation. On this basis the heavy structure produced by long unbroken polyamide chains with many bonds
to adjacent chains and the weak structure produced by
highly dispersed amide groups after prolonged reaction are
fairly obvious. This reduced bonding with dispersed amide
groups can be explained on the basis of deactivation or
steric hindrance. The existence of hydrogen bonding with
nylon-type polyamides is well substantiated as taking place
between the NH and CO groups on adjacent molecules.

The idealized molecule of a thixotropic alkyd would be:

$$\sim\!\sim\!\sim \underset{\underset{H}{|}}{N}\!-\!\underset{\underset{O}{\|}}{C} \sim\!\sim\!\sim\!\sim$$

$$\begin{matrix} \cdot & \cdot \\ \cdot & \cdot \\ \cdot & \cdot \end{matrix}$$

$$\sim\!\sim\!\sim \underset{\underset{C}{\|}}{O} \ \underset{\underset{N}{|}}{H} \sim\!\sim\!\sim$$

Polyamide alkyds are used principally in brushing-type paints such as wall finishes, etc.

Isocyanate Alkyds

Alkyd resins contain hydroxyl and carboxyl end groups. Since these are hydrophilic in nature they lower the water resistance of the alkyd. By reacting with isocyanates, these end groups are covered and water resistance and abrasion resistance are improved. Since the hydroxy groups are much more reactive than the carboxyl, these are reacted to a greater extent.

Reaction to form a urethane is as follows:

$$\mathrm{RNCO + HO - Alkyd \longrightarrow RN\!-\!C\!-\!O\!-\!Alkyd}$$
$$\qquad\qquad\qquad\qquad\quad \overset{\mathrm{H}}{|}\ \overset{\mathrm{O}}{\|}$$

These are results obtained by treating alkyds with isocyanates.[*]

1. Using Nacconate 80 [†] (tolylene diisocyanate isomeric mixture), 2 per cent of Nacconate 80 based on the total solids of the resin is added to the alkyd and the mixture is allowed to stand 24 hr. A stoichiometric quantity of butanol is then added as a stabilizer against gelation. The following table shows the effect of this on the alkyds shown.

[*] Courtesy National Aniline Co.
[†] National Aniline Co.

| | Films cast on glass | | Film sprayed on untreated steel panels | Dip-coated cold-rolled steel panels |
	Dry Time Hr	Sward Hardness	Taber Index CS-17 1000 g 1000 cycles	Time to coating failure in 5% NaOH
Plaskon 3150 *				
(46% soya)	1-2	18	99.2	5-10 min
Nacconate 80 added	½-1	24	52.5	1 hr
Plaskon 3178				
(63% soya)	3-4	14	70.3	10 min
Nacconate 80 added	2	18	59.9	2 hr
Plaskon 3185				
(50% soya)	3-4	10	96.4	5-10 min
Nacconate 80 added	2	16	19.2	1 hr

* Trade-mark, Plaskon Div., Libby Owens Ford Co.

2. Upgrading of an experimental tall oil alkyd produced from tall oil acids, tetrahydrophthalic anhydride and pentaerythritol using castor oil adduct (1 mole castor oil and 3 moles Nacconate 80).

Alkyd	Dust Free	Dry Time Tack-Free	Dry Through	Full Hardness
Tall oil alkyd	4½ hr	7 hr	22 hr	42 hr
With 10% Nacconate 80	1¼ hr	2½ hr	14½ hr	23 hr

References

1. "Abitol—A Primary Alcohol" Hercules Powder Co., 1958.
2. Furber, B., *Paint Ind.*, **74**, No. 10, 10 (October 1959).
3. Garland, J. R., and Werthan, S., *Am. Paint J.*, **44**, No. 40, 86 (1960).
4. Kraft, W. M., *Paint Ind.*, **74**, No. 10, 16 (October 1959).
5. North, A. G., *J. Oil & Colour Chemists' Assoc.*, **39**, No. 9, 696 (1956).
6. Somerville, D. R., and Herr, O. S., *Ind. Eng. Chem.*, **49**, 1080 (1957).

The preferred method is the styrenation of the alkyd directly. In this case the monomer, plus a peroxide catalyst, is added to the alkyd and refluxed until proper viscosity is reached. The alkyd must not be near the gel point or it will gel during the styrenation process. All types of alkyds have been styrenated; however, it has been found that those containing at least a portion of conjugated double bonds form a clear film. Styrenated alkyds usually contain some tung oil or dehydrated castor oil.

Reaction Between Styrene and Alkyd

The type of reaction between the fatty ester and the styrene is not completely known. Many investigators have published results of studies of this reaction. There is considerable disagreement regarding whether or not the fatty esters are completely bound to the polystyrene. The entire picture has been made more complex by the variety of conditions under which the reaction has been carried out.

In 1946, Armitage [1] described the process for reacting styrene with drying oils (castor and linseed oils). Based upon examination of the reaction products, the course of this reaction was proposed to be as follows:

a. Styrene copolymerizes with the fatty esters containing conjugated unsaturation in the same manner as does butadiene by proceeding largely by 1,4 addition across the conjugated double bonds.

b. Styrene is also bound to the nonconjugated unsaturated esters through chain transfer.

c. The molecular weight of the polymer or copolymer is lower than that of regular polystyrene because of the modifying action of the fatty acids.

Brunner and Tucker [4] heated styrene with tung oil and with dehydrated castor oil in xylene solution at reflux temperature without a catalyst. From the tung oil they obtained a mixture of a copolymer comprising about eight styrene molecules for each eleostearate unit and a low molecular product with one mole styrene to one mole ester. With the dehydrated castor oil they found no evidence of a combination of polystyrene and fatty ester.

Kappelmeir [8] saponified styrenated oil and alkyds, then separated the acidified products by extraction with alcohols of increasing molecular weight. He concluded that all the polystyrene was combined with fatty acids.

Petit and Fournier [9] studied the products of the styrenation of linseed oil using benzoyl peroxide as the catalyst. They saponified the reaction products and separated the acids from polystyrene. They concluded that there was no combination of polystyrene and oil.

Schroeder and Terrill [12] found that both raw and blown linseed oil combined with styrene under polymerization conditions.

Falkenburg, Hill, and Wolf [5] studied the reaction of styrene with oils as well as the methyl esters of most of the common fatty acids. They concluded that styrene did not copolymerize with the esters, and the homogeneity of the product was no criterion of copolymerization.

Harrison and Tolberg [7] studied the polymerization of styrene with several different fatty esters using benzoyl peroxide as the catalyst. They concluded that styrene does copolymerize with fatty esters which have conjugated unsaturation, and that the composition of this polymer is about 90 parts of styrene to 10 parts of ester in the copolymer. Also, that the nonconjugated fatty esters behave chiefly as chain modifiers and reduce the molecular weight of the polymer. The saturated and mono-unsaturated esters behave in a neutral fashion, serving as solvents for the monomer and polymer.

Bobalek, *et al.* [3] used radioactive tracers to study the reaction of styrene with dehydrated castor oil. They concluded that a large portion of the styrene is present as neutral polystyrene and that 90 per cent of the fatty acids, as *p*-eleo-stearic acid, were combined with 25 per cent of the styrene.

Formulation with Styrenated Alkyds

Table 10.2 shows properties of various styrenated 60 per cent oil length alkyds. These oils varied in iodine value and conjugation. The best oil combination appeared to be a 50:50 mixture of soya and dehydrated castor oil. The linseed oil product was clear but its viscosity was very low. Heterogeneous products were obtained from the styrenation of a soybean oil alkyd, of a 90:10 soybean-dehydrated castor oil alkyd, and a 75:25 lauric acid-dehydrated castor oil alkyd.

TABLE 10.2. EFFECT OF COMPOSITION OF OIL IN 60% OIL LENGTH ALKYDS ON STYRENATION.*

	Alkyd Characteristics				Styrenated Alkyd Characteristics			
Oil Compo-sition %	Acid Value	Viscosity at 60% T.S.	Alkyd: Styrene	Hours of Sty-renation	% Con-version	Soln. Appear. @ 50% T.S.	Visc. @ 50% T.S.	Baked Film
Lauric-D.C.O. 75-25	14.3	B	1:1	6	100	Two Layers	G-H	Very Hazy
Soybean 100	17.8	A	"	"	95	Clear	E	Hazy
Soy-D.C.O. 90-10	15.1	B-C	"	"	92½	"	F-G	"
Soy-D.C.O. 75-25	14.2	D-E	"	"	94	"	H-I	Clear
Soy-D.C.O. 50-50	13.7	G-H	"	"	97	"	V-W	"
D.C.O. 100	13.5	W-X	"	¼	Gel	—	—	—
Linseed 100	14.7	B	"	6	89	Clear	D-E	Clear

* Courtesy Monsanto Chemical Co.

The styrenation of a dehydrated castor oil alkyd resulted in a gel after fifteen minutes, indicating the high reactivity of this highly conjugated oil.

A typical styrenated alkyd is as follows:

Oil	32%
NVM	50%
Solvent	Xylene
Viscosity	O-R
Color	8
Weight per gallon	8.00 lb

Such a styrenated alkyd is fast setting and dries rapidly to give films that possess excellent durability, hardness, gloss, color and color retention.

Styrenated alkyds have inherently poor solvent resistance and present a problem in recoating. Air-dried finishes made with this styrenated alkyd may be recoated in 30 to 120 min or after 48 hours.

This type of alkyd is used in:

Metal cabinet enamels
One-coat hammer finishes
Toy enamels
Farm implement enamels
Wood furniture clears

Compatibility with:

Pigments	Good
Nitrocellulose	Poor
Alkyds —short	Fair
medium	None
long	None
Varnishes—short	Fair
medium	None
long	None
Oils	Fair
Bodied oils	None

Drying and drier recommendations:

Air dry, set	5-15 min
Air dry, hard	90 min
Bake	15-30 min @ 300°F

	Air Dry	Bake
Lead	0.2 -0.4%	None
Manganese	0.02-0.04%	0.03%
Cobalt	0.02-0.04%	None

Paint formulations:

White Cabinet Enamel

Lb	Gal		
165	4.7	Titanium calcium	⎫
115	3.8	Titanium dioxide	⎪
1	0.1	Lecithin	⎬ Roller mill
161	20.1	Styrenated alkyd	⎪
8	1.0	Pine oil	⎪
58	8.0	Xylene	⎭
372	46.0	Styrenated alkyd	
65	9.0	Xylene	
56	9.0	C-8 naphtha	
1	0.1	Guaiacol solution	
4	0.4	24% Lead naphthenate	
3	0.4	6% Cobalt naphthenate	
1019	102.6		

Weight per gallon	9.87 lb
Viscosity, No. 4 Ford Cup—49 sec	
Air dry, hard	30-35 min
Gloss, 60° meter	90

Green Hammer Enamel

Lb	Gal		
20	1.70	Nonleafing aluminum	⎫
9	.80	Solfast green	⎬ Mix
32	4.00	Styrenated alkyd	⎭
607	75.5	Styrenated alkyd	
7	1.0	Mineral oil	
2	0.25	Silicone solution	
58	8.0	Xylene	
50	8.0	C-8 naphtha	
5	0.65	6% Cobalt naphthenate	
1	0.10	Guaiacol solution	
791	100.00		

Weight per gallon   7.90 lb
Air-dry, force-dry or bake
Spray, full body

Figure 10.1. Hammer finish using a styrenated alkyd. (*Courtesy Sherwin-Williams Co.*)

Vinyl Toluene

Vinyl toluene is sometimes used in place of styrene because of its greater compatibility with alkyds. The presence of the methyl group increases solubility and it can be used with soft or semidrying oils. A laboratory procedure for preparing a vinyl toluene copolymer of an oil-modified alkyd resin is shown below:

Vinyl Toluene Modified Linseed Alkyd *

	Composition		
Oil-modified alkyd			60%
	Wt. %		
Linseed fatty acids	44.5	1.0	
Glycerin	22.0	4.4	
Phthalic anhydride	33.5	2.84	
Vinyl toluene			40%
Di-tert-butyl peroxide (2% based on monomer)			

* Courtesy Dow Chemical Co.

Alkyd Preparation

Linseed fatty acids	667.5 g
Glycerin	330.0 g
Phthalic anhydride	502.5 g

Charge the fatty acids, glycerin, and phthalic anhydride into a three liter, three-neck flask equipped with agitator, thermometer and a reflux condenser containing a water separator. Fill the water trap with mineral spirits and permit a small additional amount of mineral spirits to overflow into the reactor to aid in water separation. Raise the temperature to 240°C and hold ±5°C until the acid number drops to 15 ±2. Reduce to 60 per cent nonvolatile with mineral spirits. Gardner-Holdt viscosity, G-H.

Vinyl Toluene Reaction

Linseed alkyd (60% nonvolatile)	1000 g
Vinyl toluene	400 g
Di-tert-butyl peroxide	8 g

Heat the alkyd to 160°C and maintain reflux while adding the mixture of vinyl toluene and catalyst in small increments or continuously over a 2-hour period. Continue heating at reflux for 4 to 5 hr. Reduce with mineral spirits to the desired viscosity.

Physical properties	
Volatile	Mineral spirits
Viscosity	P-Q @ 50% NVM
Mineral spirits (35 K.B.)	
solubility	Infinite
Acid no.	5-7
Color, Gardner	6-7
Air dry (0.03% cobalt drier)	
To touch	25 min
To hard	3-4 hr
Sward hardness	
24 hr	15%
7 days	18%
1 month	18%

Flexibility
  ⅛" Mandrel   Failed
  ¼" Mandrel   Passed

Miscellaneous Monomers

Methyl methacrylate is sometimes used as a modifier for alkyd resins. These alkyds are featured by rapid curing (whether air-dried or baked), color retention, durability, and toughness. The methacrylation [11] of alkyds gives homogeneous products only in the case of dehydrated castor oil, alkyds from nonconjugated oils mixed with dehydrated castor oil, tung oil or oiticica oil, and alkyds of short oil length from linseed oil. Oil lengths for dehydrated castor oil appear to be limited to the range of 15 to 55 per cent, and aromatic solvents are essential for a homogeneous product. A workable range of 20 to 70 per cent methyl methacrylate appears possible.

F. Benner, *et al.*[2] modified 50 per cent soya-dehydrated castor oil alkyds with 2:1, 1:1, and 1:2 ratios of methyl methacrylate to alkyd, but only a 2:1 modification resulted in a significant change in the properties of the alkyd, such as increased drying rate, hardness and viscosity. The color, acid number and clarity decreased. These investigators also reported they were able to incorporate only up to 6.2 per cent acrylonitrile into an alkyd. With this small amount none of the modified resins exhibited film properties significantly different from those of the basic resin.

Combinations of monomers are sometimes used to attain specific properties. Such modifications are faster drying than conventional alkyds. Vinyl toluene imparts solubility, acrylonitrile gives toughness and resistance to solvents and oils, and methyl methacrylate improves durability.

J. C. Petropoulos, *et al.*[10] studied the addition of acrylonitrile to a styrenated alkyd. They found that acrylonitrile as a partial replacement for styrene or methyl styrene in styrenated alkyds markedly improved the resistance of films to mineral spirits, increased drying speed, improved film clarity at low acrylonitrile levels, reduced bronzing and chalking in the pigmented film during early stages of exterior exposure, and increased resin viscosity. Interpolymers having better film properties were obtained using the linseed-modified alkyd, than with a similar tall oil fatty acid alkyd. Acrylonitrile seems to promote more co-reaction between growing polymer chains and alkyd resins than that which occurs in its absence.

F. Benner, *et al.*[2] also studied modification of alkyds with styrene and acrylonitrile and found that at the modification range of 50 per cent with mixtures of styrene to acrylonitrile of 3:1 or better, the modification resulted in greatly improved drying and hardness. The flexibility and solvent resistance of the alkyd were decreased slightly.

References

1. Armitage, F. J., and Hewitt, D. H., *J. Oil & Colour Chemists' Assoc.*, **29**, 109-29 (1946).
2. Benner, F., *et al., Offic. Dig.*, **31**, 1143 (1959).
3. Bobalek, E. G., *et al., Anal. Chem.*, **28**, 906-08 (1956).
4. Brunner, H., and Tucker, D. R., *J. Appl. Chem.*, **1**, 563-68 (1951).
5. Falkenburg, L. B., Hill, W. H., Wolf, H., *J. Am. Oil Chemists' Soc.*, **28**, 496-98 (1951).
6. Falkenburg, L. B., Hill, W. H., Wolf, H., *J. Am. Oil Chemists' Soc.*, **29**, 7-11 (1952).
7. Harrison, S. A., and Tolberg, W. E., *J. Am. Oil Chemists' Soc.*, **30**, 114-17 (1953).
8. Kappelmeir, C., *Paint, Oil Chem. Rev.*, **114**, 3, 16-19 (1951).
9. Petit, J., and Fournier, P., *Offic. Dig.*, **307**, 604-14 (1950).
10. Petropoulos, J. C., *et al., Ind. Eng. Chem.*, **49**, 379-82 (1957).
11. "The Methacrylation of Alkyd Resins," Rohm & Haas Co. (1958).
12. Schroeder, H. M., and Terrill, R. L., *J. Am. Oil Chemists' Soc.*, **26**, 153-57 (1949).
13. Armitage, F., and Sleightholme, J. J. (to Sherwin-Williams Co.), U. S. Patent 2,586,593 (Feb. 19, 1952).

14. Armitage, F., and Fry, E. S. J. (to Sherwin-Williams Co.), U. S. Patent 2,589,655 (Mar. 18, 1952).

15. Armitage, F., U. S. Patent 2,676,159 (Apr. 20, 1954).

16. Beavers, E. M., and Urban, R. S. (to Rohm & Haas Co.), U. S. Patent 2,727,870 (Dec. 20, 1955).

17. Bobalek, E. C. (to The Arco Co.), U. S. Patent 2,470,757 (May 24, 1949).

18. Brunner, H. (to Imperial Chemical Industries, Ltd.), U. S. Patent 2,736,715 (Feb. 28, 1956).

19. Cadwell, L. E., and Petropoulos, J. C. (to American Cyanamid Co.), U. S. Patent 2,713,039 (July 12, 1955).

20. Chapin, E. C. (to Monsanto Chemical Co.), U. S. Patent 2,-862,898 (Dec. 2, 1958).

21. Christenson, R. M. (to Pittsburgh Plate Glass Co.), U. S. Patent 2,865,874 (Dec. 23, 1958).

22. Daniel, J. H., Jr., and Petropoulos, J. C. (to American Cyanamid Co.), U. S. Patent 2,600,623 (June 17, 1952).

23. Daniel, J. H., Jr., and Corkum, R. T. (to American Cyanamid Co.), U. S. Patent 2,748,092 (May 29, 1956).

24. Griess, G. A., and Strandskov, C. V. (to Dow Chemical Co.), U. S. Patent 2,639,270 (May 19, 1953).

25. Griess, G. A., and Strandskov, C. V. (to Dow Chemical Co.), U. S. Patent 2,639,271 (May 19, 1953).

26. Griess, G. A., and Teot, A. S. (to Dow Chemical Co.), U. S. Patent 2,639,272 (May 19, 1953).

27. Hammond, W. T. C. (to Sherwin-Williams Co.), U. S. Patent 2,563,784 (Aug. 7, 1951).

28. Hewitt, D. H., and Armitage, F. (to Sherwin-Williams Co.), U. S. Patent 2,586,652 (Feb. 19, 1952).

29. Kropa, E. L. (to American Cyanamid Co.), U. S. Patent 2,-485,294 (Oct. 18, 1949).

30. Marling, P. E. (to Monsanto Chemical Co.), U. S. Patent 2,606,161 (Aug. 5, 1952).

31. Meeshe, C. J., and Lagenis, D. (to Reichhold Chemicals, Inc.), U. S. Patent 2,647,092 (July 28, 1953).

32. Opp, C. J., and Werner, R. E. (to Interchemical Corp.), U. S. Patent 2,647,093 (July 28, 1953).

33. Opp, C. J., and Werner, R. E. (to Interchemical Corp.), U. S. Patent 2,647,095 (July 28, 1953).

34. Petropoulos, J. C. (to American Cyanamid Co.), U. S. Patent 2,851,431 (Sept. 9, 1958).

35. Schmutzler, A. F. (to American Cyanamid Co.), U. S. Patent 2,590,654 (Mar. 25, 1952).
36. Spellberg, N. (to Sherwin-Williams Co.), U. S. Patent 2,749,320 (June 5, 1956).
37. Sorenson, B. E. (to E. I. duPont de Nemours & Co.), U. S. Patent 2,343,483 (Mar. 7, 1944).
38. Wakeford, L. E., and Hewitt, D. H., U. S. Patent 2,392,710 (Jan. 1, 1946).
39. Yuska, H., and Hanle, J. E. (to Interchemical Corp.), U. S. Patent 2,684,345 (July 20, 1954).

11. ALKYDS BLENDED WITH OTHER MATERIALS

Alkyds can be blended with numerous other materials for use in protective coatings. In this chapter we are referring to materials that are cold blended in the process of making the coating composition rather than modifiers which are cooked directly with the alkyd. In some cases, such as with phenolics, silicones, etc., both methods can be used.

Because of their wide range of properties, alkyds can be formulated to be compatible with many diverse polymers. They impart such properties as air and baking conversion, plasticization, adhesion, improved durability, etc. Conversely, the modifying polymers sometimes impart faster drying characteristics and toughness. Some well-known examples of modification are combinations of alkyds with nitrocellulose. The alkyd contributes durability and flexibility; the nitrocellulose fast drying and toughness. Amino resin-alkyd combinations are well known for baking-type finishes for appliances, etc. The amino resin contributes hardness and rapid-baking characteristics, the alkyd contributes plasticizing properties and adhesion. Alkyds are also used in combination with vinyl resins, chlorinated rubber, synthetic rubber, and chlorinated paraffins with these polymers contributing toughness and rapid-drying properties. Alkyds have been used in conjunction with styrene-butadiene, polyvinyl acetate and other latices to improve adhesion.

Nitrocellulose-Alkyd Combinations

This is one of the earliest applications of an alkyd resin with another material. Both oxidizing and nonoxidizing alkyds are used to modify nitrocellulose lacquers. The amount and type of modifier used depends on the particular application. The usual ratio is 30 to 70 per cent of alkyd to 70 to 30 per cent nitrocellulose. The high proportion of alkyd will give softer films with better cold-check resistance but with excessive dirt pick-up and poorer water resistance.

The nondrying types of alkyds are more generally used. The addition of a hard resin such as dammar or rosin derivatives increases the hardness but adversely affects the cold-check resistance, outdoor exposure and humidity resistance. Small additions of urea or melamine resins increase hardness without any marked change in cold-check resistance and without affecting outdoor exposure adversely.

Oxidizing-type alkyds give satisfactory hardness and cold-check resistance. However, oxidizing resins when used as the major constituent have a tendency to lift on the second coat application. This lifting tendency can be minimized by including some nonoxidizing alkyd in the formula.

Nondrying short-oil glyceryl phthalate alkyds are pale in color, nonyellowing, and can be used in white lacquers. This type of material is used in automotive finishing lacquers and has excellent durability.

Long-oil drying-type alkyds are usually not compatible with nitrocellulose. The short to medium drying oil drying types can be used in many applications if the lifting behavior is kept in mind.

Alkyd-Amino Resin Combinations

The designation "amino resins" is a convenient term to apply to a class of resins based chiefly on urea-formaldehyde and melamine-formaldehyde condensation products. The urea-formaldehyde resins were introduced to the protective coatings industry in 1936 and the melamine-formaldehyde resins in 1940. Amino resins are of the heat-convertible type and are used in baking finishes and occasionally in air-drying coatings. When baked alone, amino resins produce hard, brittle films with poor adhesion. The amino resins first produced were soluble in water and alcohols. It was found that modification with aliphatic alcohols imparted compatibility with alkyd resins and solubility in organic solvents such as butanol, xylene, and mineral spirits. The most commonly used alcohol is butyl alcohol, so these resins are sometimes called butylated urea-formaldehyde resins. The butyl alcohol is tied into the polymer through an ether linkage.

Figure 11.1. Aluminum siding finished with baked alkyd-amino resin coating.

The mechanism of the cure of amino coatings has neither been firmly proved nor established.[2] The cure of amino resins by themselves is slow. The addition of a small amount of acid will speed the cure in the baking range of 100 to 450°F. When cured in combination with alkyd resins the reaction is more rapid. One theory proposed is that of trans-etherification. Alkyd resins high in hydroxyl content are more useful with amino resins. It may be that the carboxyl acid groups also promote curing.

By changing the proportions of melamine, formaldehyde

and butyl alcohol, it is possible to obtain polymers with varying degrees of solubility and cure. Replacement of a portion of the butanol with higher alcohols, such as octyl, improves compatibility with longer oil alkyds.

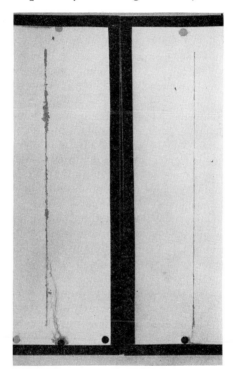

Figure 11.2. Two-hundred-hour salt-spray exposure tests. (Left: competitive coating. Right: alkyd-amino coating.)

The amount of amino resin to alkyd resin can vary from 5 to 50 per cent. In automotive finishes low amounts of amino resin, from 5 to 10 per cent, are used. Appliance finishes usually run 30 to 40 per cent, and some low-bake catalyzed furniture finishes as high as 50 per cent amino resin.

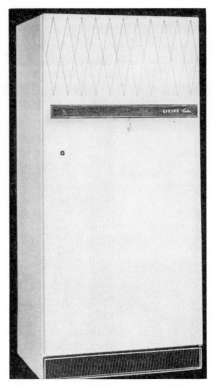

Figure 11.3. Most appliance finishes are based on alkyd-amino resin systems. (*Courtesy Gibson Refrigerator Div.*)

A comparison of the performance properties of urea versus melamine shows that:

Melamine resins cure faster.

Melamine resins impart better soap and alkali resistance, durability and color retention at higher temperatures.

Urea resins are lower in cost.

Alkyd-amino coatings are used for automotive finishes. These finishes are usually baked for 30 to 45 minutes at 275

TABLE 11.1. SWARD HARDNESS OF BAKED ENAMELS.*

% Urea or Melamine (remainder alkyd)	Nonoxidizing Coconut Oil Alkyd		Oxidizing Soya Oil Modification		Oxidizing Dehydrated Castor Oil Modification	
	Urea	Melamine	Urea	Melamine	Urea	Melamine
10	6	10	5	8	9	14
20	12	17	12	17	15	22
30	15	26	16	28	18	35
40	19	29	18	37	21	40

Pigment-Binder ratio, 0.9 to 1.0
Pigment, Titanox RA

* Courtesy Titanium Pigments Corp.

TABLE 11.2. IMPACT RESISTANCE [1] OF ALKYD-AMINO
BAKED ENAMELS.*

% Urea or Melamine (remainder alkyd)	Nonoxidizing Coconut Oil Alkyd		Oxidizing Soya Oil Modification		Oxidizing Dehydrated Castor Oil Modification	
	Urea	Melamine	Urea	Melamine	Urea	Melamine
10	15	13	35	34	35	35
20	10	6	35	14	34	18
30	7	3	31	4	30	6
40	2	2	18	3	20	2

Pigment-Binder ratio, 0.9 to 1.0
Pigment, Titanox PA
[1] Inch lbs.

* Courtesy Titanium Pigments Corp.

TABLE 11.3. EFFECT OF VEHICLE COMPOSITION ON GLOSS
OF BAKED ENAMEL.*

% Nonoxidizing Alkyd	% Oxidizing Alkyd	% Urea	% Melamine	20° Gloss, %
80	0	20	0	27
80	0	10	10	67
50	30	20	0	70
50	30	10	10	73
60	0	0	40	40
60	0	30	10	65
50	10	30	10	65

Pigment, Titanox RA @ 20 PVC

* Courtesy Titanium Pigments Corp.

to 300°F. The amino resin prevents wrinkling of the finish and improves scratch resistance and durability.

Table 11.1 shows the film hardness attained with various amounts of urea and melamine resins. As the amount of amino resin is increased the impact resistance of a baked enamel is decreased, as shown in Table 11.2.

Table 11.3 shows the effect of the addition of amino resins on gloss.

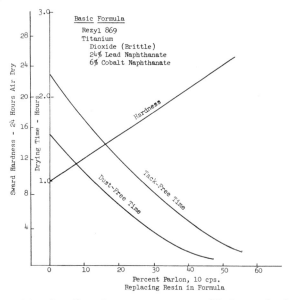

Figure 11.4. The effect of increasing amounts of Parlon on the drying time and hardness of a typical alkyd finish. (*Courtesy Hercules Powder Co.*)

Alkyd-Chlorinated Rubber Blends

Chlorinated rubber imparts fast drying, toughness, chemical resistance, and fire-retardant properties when used in combination with alkyds. For this reason, paints containing alkyds in combination with chlorinated rubber are used for

TABLE 11.4.* PARLON †—DRYING ALKYD ENAMELS.

Materials	Formula #1	Formula #2	Formula #3	Formula #4
Stabilized Parlon 5 c.p.	7.9	—	—	—
Stabilized Parlon 10 c.p.	—	6.9	5.5	8.9
Duraplex ‡ D65A (85%)	27.8	24.3	—	25.5
Duraplex ‡ C55 (70%)	—	—	16.3	—
Titanium dioxide R-610 †	22.3	19.41	15.3	21.5
Zinc oxide	—	—	—	2.4
Lampblack	0.48	0.40	0.30	0.40
Xylene	22.70	26.8	33.97	—
Hi-flash naphtha	12.3	14.6	18.6	32.73
Turpentine	6.20	7.3	9.3	8.3
5% Calcium naphthenate	—	—	0.43	—
6% Cobalt naphthenate	0.11	0.10	0.14	0.17
6% Manganese naphthenate	0.11	0.10	—	—
Epichlorohydrin	0.04	0.04	0.03	0.05
National Aniline ASA	0.06	0.05	0.04	0.05
Antiflooding agent (2% GE 81069 in xylene)	—	—	0.04	—
	100.00	100.00	100.00	100.00
Total solids, % by weight	54	47	38	55
Pigment to vehicle ratio (by weight)	1:1.38	1:1.38	1:1.38	1:1.25
Parlon to alkyd ratio (by weight)	25:75	25:75	25:75	29:71
Viscosity, No. 4 Ford Cup, seconds	27	18	17	65
Tack-free drying time	1-2 hr	1-2 hr	¾-1 hr	1 hr
Elongation conical mandrel (after 72 hr drying)	> 30%	> 30%	> 30%	> 30%

* Courtesy Hercules Powder Co.
† Trade-mark, Hercules Powder Co.
‡ Trade name, Rohm & Haas Co.

traffic paints, maintenance paints, machinery enamels, and other fast-drying enamels, and fire-retardant paints.

Chlorinated rubber is an excellent modifier for medium to long oil alkyds and certain nondrying alkyds. It is used in amounts from 5 to 67 per cent of the vehicle solids. The

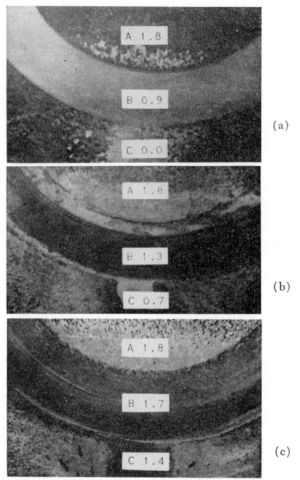

Figure 11.5. Abrasion and alkali resistance of Parlon-alkyd finishes.
(*Courtesy Hercules Powder Co.*)

(a) Unmodified alkyd finish. 100% of film was removed by the alkaline drip. 50% of film was removed by the scrubbing.

(b) 25:75 Parlon-alkyd finish. 60% of film was removed by the alkaline drip. 28% of film was removed by the scrubbing.

(c) 33:67 Parlon-alkyd finish. 22% of film was removed by the alkaline drip. 6% of film was removed by the scrubbing.

proper amount to use is controlled by such properties as drying time and chemical resistance. Since chlorinated rubber is available in a wide range of viscosity types, various combinations are possible. The low-viscosity types have better compatibility and spraying characteristics than the higher viscosity types. When amounts as high as 40 per cent of the vehicle solids are used, the addition of a plasticizer such as dibutyl phthalate is desirable.

Figure 11.4 shows the effect of increasing amounts of chlorinated rubber on the drying time and hardness of a typical alkyd finish. Both dust-free and tack-free drying times are decreased and hardness increased by increasing amounts of chlorinated rubber. Parlon *-modified alkyd-enamel formulations are shown in Table 11.4.

Exterior durability of alkyds is not affected by the addition of chlorinated rubber. Salt-spray resistance is improved and for this reason it finds use in metal primers. Improved abrasion resistance and good resistance to alkaline cleaning compounds is attained. Figure 11.5 shows improvement in

Figure 11.6. Traffic paint tests. Most traffic paints are based on alkyd or alkyd-chlorinated rubber formulas. (*Courtesy Sherwin-Williams Co.*)

* Trade-mark, Hercules Powder Co.

alkali and abrasion resistance of an alkyd resin by the addition of chlorinated rubber.

An important application of chlorinated rubber-alkyd combinations is their use in traffic paints (Figure 11.6). This application utilizes the fast drying and good abrasion resistance of these materials. C. W. Gault [4] found from extensive tests on traffic paint that a chlorinated rubber, 65 per cent soya pentaerythritol alkyd gave the best performance.

Alkyd-Vinyl Combinations

The combination of vinyl resins with alkyd resin imparts to the coating the toughness of the vinyl along with the

Figure 11.7. Alkyd-type insulating varnishes. (*Courtesy Sherwin-Williams Co.*)

good adhesion of the alkyd. Coatings of this type are used by the Navy [2] as topside coatings. These are applied over vinyl wash primers. Poor adhesion has been the primary problem characteristic of pure vinyl finishes. It has been found that modification of vinyls with considerable quantities of alkyd resin affords a marked improvement in this respect. It has been found that about a 60 per cent oil alkyd gives optimum results. It is used in proportions of 35 per cent vinyl resin with 65 per cent alkyd. The type of oil used in the alkyd does not seem critical; good formulations have been attained with soya, linseed and dehydrated castor.

Alkyd-Silicone Combinations

Alkyd-silicone combinations are used for air drying or baking insulating varnish applications where high-temperature resistance is desired (Figure 11.7). These materials have good water and chemical resistance. Shown below are resistance tests comparing a straight silicone coating with an alkyd-silicone coating:

Immersion Tests	Alkyd-Silicone Two coats, each baked 3 hr @ 300°F on 5-mil copper	100% Silicone Two coats, each baked 9 hr @ 400°F on 5-mil copper
10% Sulfuric acid, 90 days, room temp.	No effect	Film lost adhesion and wrinkled badly.
10% Vegetable fatty acids 72 hr, room temp.	No effect	Attacked film and panel.
Toluene, 72 hr, room temp.	No effect	Film lifted.
Transformer oil, 96 hr, 300°F	No effect	Oil-degraded and film-softened.

The combination of silicone resins with alkyd resins gives a material with improved heat and water resistance over a conventional alkyd resin and with improved adhesion over the silicone resin. Vehicles composed of 75 per cent silicone and 25 per cent alkyd have good color retention at temperatures up to 450°F and good exterior durability. Alkyds composed of 25 per cent silicone resin and 75 per cent alkyd resin have good color retention at temperatures up to 400°F and good adhesion. Silicone modified alkyds show very good gloss retention on exposure.

A typical formula is shown below:

Flat Black High Heat-Resistant Paint [*]

	Pounds per 100 Gallons	
	50/50	25/75
Material	Silicone Alkyd	Silicone Alkyd
5X Asbestine	76.3	72.9
Drackenfeld #10035 Black	310.5	296.5
Aroplaz 7310	305.0	438.0
G.E. Silicone Resin SR-82 (60% NVM)	254.0	121.8
Solvesso 100	129.5	123.8
Xylene	37.0	35.0
8% Zinc octoate	3.9	1.9
6% Cobalt octoate	1.0	1.4
6% Manganese octoate	1.0	1.4
	1118.2	1092.7
Weight per gallon—lb	11.2	10.9
Viscosity, K. U.	60	70

* Courtesy General Electric Co.

Both of these paints withstood 65 to 70 hours at 725°F while still retaining film integrity. They would not tolerate much bending but this is to be expected. On rigid surfaces the degree of retained film integrity over an extended period at high temperatures would depend on the silicone content.

These paints will air dry if baking prior to service is not possible, but the best early film is obtained after an initial bake of 30 to 45 minutes at 300 to 400°F.

Alkyd-Synthetic Latex Combinations

Alkyds are blended with synthetic latices such as styrene-butadiene, polyvinyl acetate, and acrylics to improve water resistance, flexibility, and adhesion. For styrene-butadiene modification, long oil alkyds are used; for polyvinyl acetate modification more polar-type alkyds are used. Viscosity should be low enough so that the alkyds can be dispersed without solvent.

A formula of this type is shown below:

Interior Emulsion Paint—Butadiene Styrene—Alkyd Modified *

(For 100 gallons of paint)

"Titanox" † RA-50	250	lb
Magnesium silicate	163	lb
Potassium tri-polyphosphate	2	lb
Alkyd resin—100% NV	5.25	gal
Butadiene-styrene emulsion	33.2	gal
Wetting agent	1.0	gal
Thickener	15.5	gal
Water	28.7	gal
24% Lead naphthenate	0.09	gal
6% Cobalt naphthenate	0.05	gal
Antifoam agent	0.2	gal
Freeze-thaw stabilizer	2.0	gal

* Courtesy Titanium Pigments Corp.
† Trade-mark, Titanium Pigments Corp.

Alkyds, because of their wide compatibility, can also be blended with drying oils, acrylics, phenolics, chlorinated paraffins, ethyl cellulose, ester gums, maleic resins, hydrocarbon resins, and other materials. Compatibility depends on the oil length and the amount used.

References

1. Brachen, W. O., *et al.*, *Offic. Dig.*, **28**, 794-815 (1956).
2. Crecelius, S. B., Naval Research Laboratory Report 4257, P. B. 111369, 1954.
3. Crecelius, S. B., Naval Research Laboratory Report 4662, P. B. 111824, 1955.
4. Gault, C. W., *et al.*, *Offic. Dig.*, **32**, 888-96 (1960).
5. Whonsiedler, H. P., Papers Presented at the New York Meeting, American Chemical Society, Division of Organic Coatings & Plastics Chemistry, **20**, No. 2, 53-63 (1960).

12. MISCELLANEOUS (SPECIAL) ALKYDS

There are many miscellaneous modifications of alkyds described in patents and literature. Although none has large volume usage, they are of sufficient interest to mention. In many cases the cost of raw materials is too high to make the product economically feasible.

Imide-Modified Alkyd Resins

Wright and Dupuis [17] prepared a series of imide-modified alkyds in which glyceryl phthalimide replaced some of the ester groups. Glyceryl phthalimide was prepared by heating equal molar ratios of glycerylamine and phthalic anhydride under an atmosphere of inert gas with agitation. After purification, the glyceryl phthalimide is a white crystalline solid.

A series of soya glycerol phthalate resins containing 20 to 35 per cent oil were all found to be soluble in aromatic solvents except the one containing 20 per cent oil. Acid number was between 10 and 14.

Film tests were made by adding 0.01 per cent cobalt drier and baking at 181°F for 20 minutes. The imide-modified alkyd films were reported to be harder and to have better water-vapor resistance and about the same color as straight ester alkyds.

Glycerol-Allyl Ether

Alkyd resins prepared from glycerol $\propto$-allyl ether are described by Bradley, et al.[2]

$$CH_2\text{—}O\text{—}CH_2\text{—}CH{=}CH_2$$
$$CHOH$$
$$CH_2OH$$

An alkyd was prepared using phthalic anhydride and glycerol $\propto$-allyl ether which was thinned to 75 per cent solids with xylene. This resin was reported to have properties equal or superior to a similar resin made with fatty acids. The air-drying finishes set to touch within six hours and were fully hardened and water resistant within seven days. The resins were better suited for baking finishes and could be cured in two hours at 150°F. The finish had good water and solvent resistance and withstood a 25-cycle cold-check test without failure. Finishes on metal could be baked at 300°F for about thirty minutes and no catalyst was required. The resin showed better color retention on heat aging than a soybean oil alkyd urea-formaldehyde combination. The replacement of the long chain fatty acid with the short ether chain made no significant difference in flexibility. This rather surprising result was attributed to the relative ease of molecular rotation of the ether oxygen linkages.

Tetrachlorophthalic Anhydride

Mehta and Payne [14] investigated the use of tetrachlorophthalic anhydride in alkyd resins and plasticizers. Linseed oil, soybean oil, and coconut oil alkyds were made, each composed of 40 per cent oil and 60 per cent glyceryl phthalate. These resins were all darker in color than comparable phthalic alkyds. There was no significant difference in air-drying time, but the water and alkali resistance were slightly better with the tetrachlorophthalic anhydride.

Fire resistance of the linseed-tetrachlorophthalic resin was compared with the linseed-phthalic resin using the National Military Establishment Specification (JAN-P-702,

November 23, 1948, Paint, Inside White Semi-Gloss Fire Retardant). The paints made with the tetrachlorophthalic alkyd were more fire retardant than the phthalic alkyd paint, but the improvement was not great. Calculations showed that the resin binder contained only 26.1 per cent chlorine, which is not sufficient for significant fire retardance. Fifty per cent chlorine is usually considered to be the minimum required.

Maleic Anhydride Adducts

Maleic anhydride can be combined with other unsaturated materials to give numerous dibasic acids. During World War II, with only a limited amount of phthalic anhydride available to the protective coatings industry, many substitutes of this type were used.

Carbic anhydride is the addition product of cyclopentadiene and maleic anhydride. Although carbic anhydride and phthalic anhydride are both cyclic anhydrides, their unsaturation is different. Carbic anhydride contains additional unsaturation which gives greater reactivity in the kettle but also poorer performance on exposure.

Petrex * is a maleic adduct of a terpene. The branch chains of the Petrex impart somewhat greater solubility in hydrocarbons but they decrease hardness.

Water Dispersible or Emulsifiable Alkyds

Because of the many advantages of emulsion paints which use a water diluent, considerable work has been done to develop alkyd systems of this type. Alkyds can be converted into water soluble or dispersible materials by treatment with ammonia, amines, or alkali. Another method is cooking a surfactant into the alkyd so that upon the addition to water it is readily dispersed.

* Trade-mark, Hercules Powder Co.

R. P. Arndt [1] reports that the incorporation of a polyethylene glycol into an alkyd resin produces a resin that is easily dispersed in water. Polyethylene glycol (10 to 30 per cent) is heated with a 30 to 60 per cent oil-modified alkyd at a temperature of 200 to 300°F for one-half to five hours. The product will air-dry, and can be dispersed in water without the use of dispersing agents.

There are numerous patents issued on water dispersible alkyds.[3, 4, 5, 6, 7, 8, 13, 15]

Miscellaneous

Several investigators have found that elimination of the terminal hydroxyl groups improves the water resistance and stability of an alkyd. Both treatment with ketene [9] ($R_2C=CO$) and acetic anhydride [10] were used.

The dispersion of up to 5 per cent lecithin in the hot alkyd resin before thindown improved the wetting characteristics of the alkyd, particularly for use in grinding pigments.[16]

References

1. Arndt, R. P. (to Pittsburgh Plate Glass Co.), U. S. Patent 2,-634,245 (Apr. 7, 1953).
2. Bradley, T. F., Dunnenberg, H., and Evans, T. F., *Ind. Eng. Chem.*, 41, 1709 (1949).
3. Cheetham, H. C. (to The Resinous Products Co.), U. S. Patent 2,272,057 (Feb. 3, 1942).
4. Cheetham, H. C., and Meyers, R. J., U. S. Patent 2,279,387 (Apr. 14, 1942).
5. Cheetham, H. C., and Meyers, R. J. (to The Resinous Products and Chemical Co.), U. S. Patent 2,308,474 (Jan. 12, 1943).
6. Christenson, R. M., Cummings, L. O., and Hart, D. P. (to Pittsburgh Plate Glass Co.), U. S. Patent 2,852,475 (July 15, 1958).
7. Christenson, R. M., and Hart, D. P. (to Pittsburgh Plate Glass Co.), U. S. Patent 2,853,459 (Sept. 23, 1958).
8. Cummings, L. O. (to Pittsburgh Plate Glass Co.), U. S. Patent 2,852,476 (Sept. 16, 1958).

9. E. I. du Pont de Nemours & Co., British Patent 419,373 (Nov. 12, 1934).

10. Fuller, C. S. (to Bell Telephone Laboratories, Inc.), U. S. Patent 2,275,260 (Mar. 10, 1942).

11. Goebel, C. G. (to Emery Industries, Inc.), U. S. Patent 2,482,761 (Sept. 27, 1949).

12. Goebel, C. G., *J. Oil & Colour Chemists' Assoc.*, **34**, 361 (1951).

13. Light, D. L. (to American Cyanamid Co.), U. S. Patent 2,-471,396 (May 24, 1949).

14. Mehta, D. J., and Payne, H. F., *Paint Varnish Production*, **30**, 6 (1950).

15. Robinson, R. S. (to Reichhold Chemicals, Inc.), U. S. Patent 2,586,092 (Feb. 19, 1952).

16. Unger, M. B. (to Sherwin-Williams Co.), U. S. Patent 2,738,337 (Mar. 13, 1956).

17. Wright, H. J., and Dupuis, R. N., *Ind. Eng. Chem.*, **38**, 1303 (1946).

13. RECENT ALKYD DEVELOPMENTS

During the past five years many new raw materials have become available for use in alkyd resins. New polyols, acids and anhydrides, fatty acids, and oils are obtainable which can be used to formulate alkyds with improved properties. Price reductions on other materials have promoted their use in alkyds.

Isophthalic Acid

Probably the most significant development [6, 7, 8] in the past few years was the commercial production of isophthalic acid, which made these materials available at prices competitive with orthophthalic anhydride. Phthalic anhydride which has been the backbone of alkyds for years is of the *ortho* form. Isophthalic acid is of the *meta* form.

The replacement of phthalic anhydride with isophthalic acid produces a harder resin with improved heat and alkali resistances. The cooking of an isophthalic alkyd is more difficult. First, because an acid is used, twice as much water is evolved from the reaction as from an anhydride. Secondly, the melting point of the acid is higher; as a result, there is less solubility in the reaction mixture. The esterification is carried out at a higher temperature.

Shown below are three soya alkyds using *ortho*, iso-, and terephthalic acid. They are 65 per cent oil and cooked at a temperature of 500°F.

	Cooking Time	Visc. @ 60% NVM	Set	Drying, Hr Tack-free
Phthalic anhydride	14	E	2¼	9
Isophthalic acid	8	W	1	3
Terephthalic acid	6	Z_5	¾	2¾

Initially the reaction rate with phthalic anhydride is faster as the first step of forming the ester from the anhydride is rapid. However, the second step of forming ester from acid groups is slower. In Figure 13.1 is shown the esterification rate of a 65 per cent soya glycerin alkyd made with 5 per cent excessive glycerin.

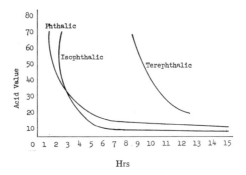

Figure 13.1. Esterification rate of a 65 per cent soya glycerin alkyd made with 5 per cent excess glycerin.

Viscosity of an isophthalic alkyd is somewhat higher than the ortho. (See Fig. 13.2.)

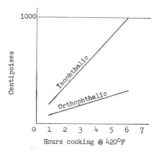

Figure 13.2. Viscosity of isophthalic alkyd and orthophthalic alkyd.

A typical isophthalic cook is as follows:

60% Soya Isophthalic Alkyd

Soya oil	420 lb
Glycerin	112 lb
Litharge	0.168 lb
Isophthalic acid	243 lb
Excess hydroxy	20%

Charge soya oil, glycerin, and litharge into kettle, hold at 450°F for 1 hr. Add isophthalic acid and heat for 6 hr. Thin to 50 per cent solids in mineral spirits.

Viscosity	Z_2
Acid value	11
NVM	50

This vehicle has the following properties:

Drying time, minutes	
Touch	40
Sward hardness	
1 day	9
28 days	28
Impact resistance in./lb	16

Isophthalic alkyds show a tendency to gel before equivalent orthophthalic alkyds indicating an "apparent higher functionality." It has been assumed that isophthalic acid has a true functionality of two reacting carboxyl groups, whereas the functionality of orthophthalic anhydride is reduced to less than two by the formation of cyclic intra-esters. While intra-esterification no doubt occurs to some extent, it has been shown that orthophthalic anhydride has a full functionality of two in simple alkyd systems. Correspondingly, isophthalic appears to have a functionality considerably greater than two. Since only two functional acid groups are present in isophthalic acid, it follows that this additional functionality in the system comes from side reactions occurring in the presence of isophthalic acid which do not take place with phthalic anhydride.

R. Brown and H. Ashjian [1] found the increased functionality to be caused by etherification of the polyol in the presence of the isophthalic acid. In trimethylethane isophthalic lauric acid alkyd systems, they found that 38 per cent of the polyol formed ethers.

Trimellitic Anhydride

Trimellitic anhydride is a trifunctional aromatic acid with the following structure:

Molecular weight	192.12
Equivalent weight	64.04
Melting point	334°F

Trimellitic anhydride is suggested for use in medium- and long-oil alkyds. Long-oil trimellitic alkyds are reported to dry faster and to a harder film than phthalic and isophthalic alkyds of the same oil length.

*Comparison of Properties of Trimellitic-Modified 60% Soya Phthalic Alkyd **

	Trimellitic-Modified 60% Soya Phthalic Alkyd	Unmodified 60% Soya Phthalic Alkyd
Trimellitic anhydride	53	—
Phthalic anhydride	236	285
Soya oil, alkali-refined	562	575
Glycerin, 96% (15% excess)	149	140
Litharge	0.3	0.3

* Courtesy of Amoco Chemicals Corp.

Charge the soybean oil and glycerin, heat to 400°F with agitation and sparge with an inert gas at the rate of 0.02 cu ft per min per gal. At 400°F add the litharge and raise the temperature to 460°F. Hold for 1 hr. Increase heat to 480°F and charge the trimellitic anhydride. Let temperature drop to 460°F and hold until acid value is 10 or less. Then add the phthalic anhydride and continue processing to a cure of 20-30 sec. Thin in mineral spirits.

	Trimellitic-Modified 60% Soya Phthalic Alkyd *	Unmodified 60% Soya Phthalic Alkyd
Viscosity, Gardner-Holdt		
60% solids in mineral spirits	Z_2-Z_4	—
80% solids in mineral spirits	—	Z_2
Color—Gardner		
60% solids in mineral spirits	4-5	—
80% solids in mineral spirits	—	6-7
Acid number—solids basis	6.5	9.2
Cure	24	104
Drying schedule—Approximately 1-mil dry film on glass:		
set to touch, hr	¾	3
set to carton, hr	2½	4
Kraft paper free, hr	4½	6
Sward hardness		
1 day	2	1
3 days	4	3
7 days	8	5
Drier combination		
naphthenates, %	0.05 Co	0.05 Co
	0.5 Pb	0.5 Pb

* Courtesy of Amoco Chemicals Corp.

Epoxidized Oils as Alkyd Modifiers

W. C. Chatfield [2] reported on the use of epoxidized oils as an ingredient for alkyds.

Epoxidized oils may be prepared from unsaturated glycerides and contain at least one epoxide group in each initially unsaturated fatty acid chain. An epoxide group reacts with organic acids to yield a diester:

$$
\begin{array}{c}
\overset{\displaystyle O}{\underset{H\ H}{\overset{\|}{+\ R\text{C}-\text{OH}}}} \\
-\underset{\diagdown\!\diagup}{\text{C}-\text{C}}- \\
\text{O}
\end{array}
\longrightarrow
\begin{array}{cc}
\text{H} & \text{H} \\
-\text{C} - & \text{C}- \\
| & | \\
\text{O} & \text{O} \\
\text{C}=\text{O} & \text{H} \\
| \\
\text{R}
\end{array}
\xrightarrow{\ +\ R\overset{O}{\overset{\|}{\text{C}}}-\text{OH}\ }
\begin{array}{cc}
\text{H} & \text{H} \\
-\text{C} - & \text{C}- \\
| & | \\
\text{O} & \text{O} \\
\text{C}=\text{O} & \text{C}=\text{O} \\
| & | \\
\text{R} & \text{R}
\end{array}
$$

The first step of the reaction is much faster than the second step. Since the usual epoxidized oil contains 3 to 4 epoxy groups, the functionality can be as high as a hexahydric or octohydric alcohol although the second hydroxyl group, being a secondary alcohol, probably does not react completely. Even when an epoxidized oil is regarded as a trihydric alcohol only, it is unique by reason of its structure and high molecular weight, which is in excess of 900.

The use of an epoxidized oil in an alkyd produces a vehicle with high viscosity and lower acid value. The replacement of 20-mole per cent of the glycerin in a 60 per cent linseed glyceryl phthalate alkyd produced an alkyd with a viscosity of 500 poises in 5.5 hr cooking as compared to 200 poises in 5.0 hr for the standard material.

Treatment of Alkyds with Aldehydes

The addition of aldehydes during the cooking of certain alkyds is reported to improve their drying properties.[4] The basic chemical reaction which occurs is one of acetal formation from the formaldehyde and pentaerythritol. Both cylic and linear structures are formed:

$$
\begin{array}{ccc}
\text{HOCH}_2 & & \text{CH}_2\text{O} \\
& \diagdown \diagup \quad \diagdown & \\
& \text{C} & \text{CH}_2 \\
& \diagup \diagdown \quad \diagup & \\
\text{HOCH}_2 & & \text{CH}_2\text{O}
\end{array}
$$

Cyclic

$$\underset{\text{Linear}}{\overset{\displaystyle \text{HOCH}_2 \quad \text{CH}_2\text{OCH}_2\text{OCH}_2 \quad \text{CH}_2\text{OH}}{\underset{\text{HOCH}_2 \quad \text{CH}_2\text{OH} \; \text{HOCH}_2 \quad \text{CH}_2\text{OH}}{\text{C} \qquad\qquad\qquad \text{C}}}}$$

This reaction appears to proceed only in the presence of an anhydride such as phthalic. The formaldehyde is incorporated into the batch on the basis of 0.5 to 0.6 mole per mole of pentaerythritol. The alkyd has improved drying characteristics with good flexibility. Such a technique would allow the use of polyols of higher functionality, such as pentaerythritol, in short-oil alkyds. A medium-oil alkyd prepared from linseed fatty acids had a foil drying time of two hours in clear films.

Tris (Hydroxymethyl) Aminomethane

Tris (hydroxymethyl) aminomethane has the following structure containing three hydroxyl groups and one amine group:

$$\text{NH}_2{-}\underset{\underset{\text{CH}_2\text{OH}}{|}}{\overset{\overset{\text{CH}_2\text{OH}}{|}}{\text{C}}}{-}\text{CH}_2\text{OH}$$

Although five reactive hydrogens are present, the *tris* (hydroxymethyl) aminomethane reacts as a trifunctional material. It is believed that one mole of fatty acid reacts with the amine forming a soap. On heating, the soap is dehydrated to the amide and then further dehydrated to a substituted oxazoline.

Attempts in controlling the reaction conditions to minimize ring formation have been unsuccessful. Two moles of water are eliminated for each fatty acid combining with the amine. However, in actual experiments the direct determination of oxazoline rings did not always check with the estimation of oxazoline rings from excess water liberated. Long [5] reported that alkyds prepared from *tris* (hydroxymethyl) aminomethane showed excellent adhesion to hydrophilic (water loving) surfaces.

Medium Oil Tris Amino Soya Alkyd *

Composition	Grams	Moles	% Weight
Tris (hydroxymethyl) aminomethane	1454	12.00	25.8
Phthalic acid anhydride	1894	12.79	33.6
Soya fatty acids	2927	10.40	51.9
	6275		111.3
Water of reaction	634	35.2	11.3
	5641		100.0

* Courtesy Commercial Solvents Corp.

Heat phthalic anyhdride and soya fatty acids to 300°F under inert gas. Add *tris* amino slowly. Raise temperature to 385°F. Hold for acid value of 8. Approximate cooking time is 5 hr. Characteristics:

NVM	50% (in mineral spirits)
Color	8
Acid value	8
Viscosity	D

Trimethylolethane and Trimethylolpropane

Trimethylolethane and trimethylolpropane are two of the newer polyols introduced in the past few years. They are produced by condensing formaldehyde with propionaldehyde and butyraldehyde respectively, and have the same neopentyl structure:

$$CH_3—\overset{\overset{\displaystyle CH_2OH}{|}}{\underset{\underset{\displaystyle CH_2OH}{|}}{CH_2OH}}$$

Trimethylolethane

$$C_2H_5—\overset{\overset{\displaystyle CH_2OH}{|}}{\underset{\underset{\displaystyle CH_2OH}{|}}{CH_2OH}}$$

Trimethylolpropane

Trimethylolpropane has been produced in Germany in commercial quantities for several years for use in polyurethane resins. It has been produced more recently in the United States and here, also, the principal use has been in polyurethanes. Trimethyolethane has been used more extensively in alkyds because its lower molecular weight and higher hydroxyl content give it an advantage costwise over trimethylolpropane. Both TME and TMP have three primary alcohol groups as compared to glycerin which has two primary and one secondary alcohol groups.

Trimethylolethane reacts rapidly in alkyd processing. Coatings produced from these alkyds exhibit outstanding color and gloss retention on exposure to heat, ultraviolet light and weather, have good compatibility and superior alkali resistance and hardness. The greatest utilization of trimethylolethane appears to be in the areas of short- and medium-oil alkyds.

In comparing polyols in alkyd formulation, three methods may be used: equal oil length, equal phthalic content, and equal molecular amounts. Kraft [3] reports on trimethyolethane and trimethylolpropane alkyds compared to glycerin alkyds using all three of the methods, as shown in Table 13.1.

From the above data it is apparent that comparable viscosities and drying times are achieved with the molecular approach and after 28 days drying, the TME and TMP alkyds are harder.

When comparison is made on the basis of equal phthalic content, the TME and TMP alkyds show higher viscosity, faster drying and greater hardness. With equal oil content, lower viscosities are obtained with the TME and TMP alkyds.

Weich [9] reported on the use of trimethylolpropane in alkyd resins. The work covered short-oil oxidizing and nonoxidizing alkyds and medium-oil oxidizing alkyds.

TABLE 13.1. TALL OIL FATTY ACID ALKYDS.*

All resins cooked @ 470°F.   Viscosity in Xylene @ 60% NVM.   Acid No. 9-10.

Polyol Approach	Glycerin —	TME Equal Molar G	TME Equal Phthalic T	TME Equal Oil E	TMP Equal Molar H	TMP Equal Phthalic P	TMP Equal Oil F
Mol ratio PA/Polyol/FA Visc. (G-H)	1/1/.70	1/1/.70	1/1/.60	1/1/.75	1/1/.70	1/1/.56	1/1/.77
Film Properties Air Dry—0.5% Pb and 0.05% Co							
Set to touch	:45	:34	:19	1:32	:40	:26	1:31
Tack-free	4:00	3:51	1:04	4:02	4:00	:55	5:01
Hardness							
1 day	4	6	8	6	6	8	4
28 days	20	34	38	32	34	36	22
Baked Films—300°F, 1 hr							
3% NaOH							
First attack	:15	8:00	3:00	8:00	5:00	3:00	8:00
Denude	86	220	269	200	195	286	187

* Courtesy Paint & Varnish Production Magazine

References

1. Brown, R., and Ashjian, H., Papers Presented at New York Meeting, American Chemical Society, Division of Organic Coatings and Plastics Chemistry, **20**, No. 2, 235-43 (1960).
2. Chatfield, W. C., *J. Oil & Colour Chemists' Assoc.*, **41**, 301 (1958).
3. Kraft, W. M., *Paint Varnish Production,* **48**, No. 11, 64 (1958).
4. Kraft, W. M., *et al., Am. Paint J.*, **44**, No. 32, 46-54 (1960).
5. Long, J. S., *J. Oil & Colour Chemists' Assoc.*, **42**, 737 (1959).
6. Miner, C. J., Jr., *Offic. Dig.*, **28**, 17-26 (1956).
7. Wampner, H. L., *Offic. Dig.*, **28**, 663-84 (1956).
8. "New York Vehicle Group Hears Experts on Isophthalic Acid," *Am. Paint J.*, **44**, No. 24, 9 (1960).
9. Weich, G. H., *Paint Varnish Production,* **50**, No. 5, 29 (1960).

14. NONCOATING APPLICATIONS

Although the principal end use of alkyds is in the protective coatings field there are lesser amounts used as plasticizers for molded and allied plastics, as printing ink vehicles, in floor coverings, adhesives, etc. There are also the so-called alkyd molding compounds which are more closely related to polyesters.

Plasticizers

Alkyds are classed as polymeric plasticizers and for the year 1958, eight per cent of all plasticizers used were of the polymeric type. These are usually esters of a dibasic acid such as adipic, sebacic, etc., reacted with ethylene, diethylene, propylene glycol, or glycerin with the chain terminated with a monobasic fatty acid.[5] These polymeric plasticizers show outstanding performance in vinyl plastics. They are usually used in combination with monomeric plasticizers to attain such properties as resistance to migration, extraction by gasoline, oil, water, soap, and detergents as well as low volatility.

Alkyd-type plasticizers are compatible with nitrocellulose, ethyl cellulose, polyvinyl butyral, polyvinyl chloride, polyvinyl acetate and chlorinated rubber. Ethel-cellulose materials of this type are used in hot-melt applications. Polyvinyl-butyral combinations have higher tensile strength than those plasticized with monomeric plasticizers. The advantage of polymeric plasticizers is that they are non-migrating and, therefore, more permanent than monomeric plasticizers.

Ink Vehicles

Alkyds are used in printing-ink vehicles. Since they are relatively slow drying they cannot be used in high-speed operations. Alkyds are used in combination with metallic pigments to give abrasive-resistant, sharp prints. A long-oil alkyd is used which does not contain solvent. Alkyds should be of low acid value so they will not react with metallic pigments. Pigments are added just prior to use.[9, 11]

Adhesives

Alkyds find some use as adhesives.[4] They have good resistance to water and fungus and are cured by solvent release or heat fusion. They show good bonding to wood, rubber, glass, leather, paper, and textiles. Applications in this field are as a binder for the abrasive in sandpaper,[1, 2] as a flock adhesive,[8] linoleum cement,[3] rubber to metal adhesive,[5] and miscellaneous applications.[6, 10]

Floor Covering

Low-cost alkyd materials have been produced for floor coatings by upgrading tall oil with maleic anhydride and then esterifying. To this mixture is added bodied soya or linseed oil.

Core Oil Resin

Low-cost alkyd resins can be used as core oil binders. Crude tall oil plus maleic anhydride is reacted, then pentaerythritol is added. To this, 20 to 30 per cent linseed oil is sometimes added.

"Alkyd Molding Compounds"

A type of material which uses the term alkyd, "alkyd molding compounds" are actually polyester resins in which styrene has been replaced by a nonvolatile monomer such as diallyl phthalate. Alkyd molding compounds are composed of a polyester resin dissolved in diallyl phthalate, plus filler, fibers and catalyst. They can be stored and handled in the same way as conventional thermosetting materials. Arc and heat resistance, dielectric qualities and dimensional stability are outstanding properties of alkyd molding compounds. Molding materials of this type cure by the peroxide-initiated free radical polymerization of the unsaturated double bonds in the allyl monomer, with the maleic or fumaric double bonds in the polymeric ester. Alkyd molding compounds liberate no volatiles during cure, exhibit good flow of the resin binder, and are fast curing.

References

1. Carlton, R. P., and Oakes, B. J. (to Minnesota Mining & Mfg. Co.), U. S. Patent 2,230,934 (Feb. 4, 1941).
2. Coes, L., Jr. (to Norton Co.), U. S. Patent 2,435,555 (Feb. 3, 1948).
3. Elliot, C. G. (to Armstrong Cork Co.), U. S. Patent 2,670,782 (Mar. 2, 1954).
4. Erickson, D. R., and Thomas, P. J., U. S. Patent 2,327,594-7 (Aug. 24, 1943).
5. Fuller, C. S. (to Bell Telephone Laboratories, Inc.), U. S. Patent 2,433,357 (Dec. 30, 1947).
6. Gold, L. J., and Zweig, S. (to Milprint, Inc.), U. S. Patent 2,446,581 (Aug. 10, 1958).
7. Koroly, J. E., and Beavers, E. M., *Ind. Eng Chem.*, 45, 1060 (1953).
8. Mitchell, R. W. (to B. B. Chemical Co.), U. S. Patent 2,511,171 (June 13, 1950).
9. "Modern Plastics Encyclopedia," 1961.
10. Roller, H. C., U. S. Patent 2,134,006 (Oct. 25, 1938).
11. Seil, H. A., and Cole, H., U. S. Patent 2,499,004 (Feb. 28, 1950).

15. FUTURE OF ALKYDS

In spite of the number of synthetic materials that have been introduced and will continue to be introduced, it seems fairly certain that alkyds will be used for many years to come. There are two reasons for this: first, the various changes that can be incorporated into an alkyd molecule through the use of new and improved raw materials in the polyhydric alcohols, polybasic acids, oils or fatty acids, and other materials; second, the ability of alkyd resins to improve the properties of other surface coating materials. Because of this they have been referred to many times as the "adaptable alkyds."

In addition to new raw materials which give improved alkyd products there are other developments which may come in the future. A continuous process for the manufacture of alkyds would increase their usage. Use of alkyds in emulsion or water systems may be extended. Each year water systems constitute a larger portion of the paint market and alkyds have not realized their share of this market. At present, processing time is between 8 to 12 hours for an alkyd resin. Catalysts or other means of reducing the cost of esterification will promote further use of alkyds.

While alkyds will not show the phenomenal growth of some of the newer materials such as epoxies in the next ten years, it is possible that they will show as much as a 20 per cent growth in this period.

INDEX